LTP PUBLICATIONS • NUMBER 6

ENLARGED PRINTS from LIBRARY MICROFORMS

a study of processes, equipment, and materials

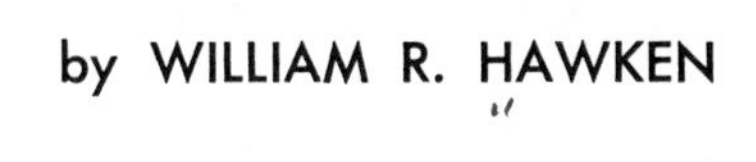

by WILLIAM R. HAWKEN

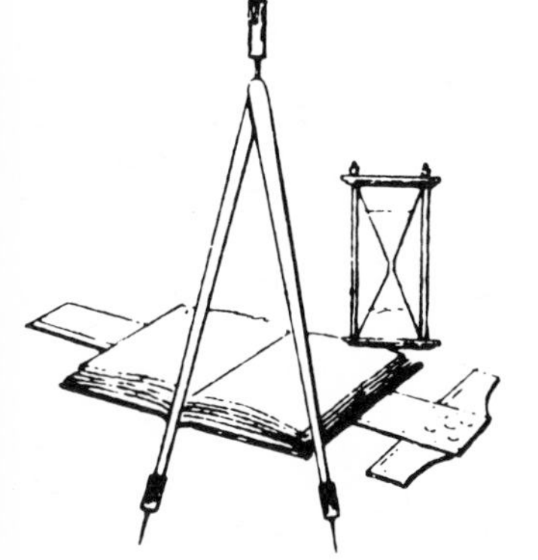

LIBRARY TECHNOLOGY PROJECT
AMERICAN LIBRARY ASSOCIATION
CHICAGO
[1963]

Library of Congress catalog number 63-15807

First printing April, 1963
Second printing July, 1963

FOREWORD

The rapid development of microfilm and other forms of microtext during the decade preceding World War II constituted a major advance in preserving and disseminating the printed word. Further progress and refinements in microforms have occurred since that time. Unfortunately, however, the full promise of these materials has not been realized, largely because the design and manufacture of equipment for making the use of microforms convenient for the student and the scholar have failed to keep pace with the development of the materials themselves. In particular, the need for devices that would make possible the production of full-size prints from microform materials quickly, economically, and without the facilities of a darkroom, has long been recognized by librarians. Yet, despite this need, the first reader-printer was not marketed until 1958.

In the year following, the American Library Association established the Library Technology Project and assigned to it the task of developing objective information on equipment and supplies suitable for library needs. The lack of data covering methods and devices for making enlarged prints from library microforms and the interest of librarians in this equipment, as evidenced by many requests for such information, led LTP to establish a program to identify the basic print-out requirements of libraries, to test and evaluate available print-out equipment in the light of these requirements, and to develop recommendations for the improvement of such equipment.

The investigation, which was made possible by a grant from the Council on Library Resources, Inc., was conducted by William R. Hawken, who for several years has been LTP's consultant on document reproduction. Mr. Hawken's technical competence and his ability to organize and present the results of his research in clear and readable style were clearly evident in *Photocopying from Bound Volumes,* his first report for the Library Technology Project. In the present report, Mr. Hawken provides a similarly careful evaluation of existing print-out equipment, an evaluation intended to assist librarians in the selection of equipment best suited to their needs. In addition, the report identifies those features that make currently available print-out devices unsuited to library purposes, and suggests modifications and improvements which would make this equipment more useful to libraries.

Although the report has been prepared primarily for librarians, it should also prove valuable to manufacturers interested in designing equipment which will better meet the needs of the nation's libraries.

Frazer G. Poole, *Director*
Library Technology Project

PREFACE

This study of reader-printers does not include all equipment of this type now on the market. It is limited to those machines which might be of potential use in libraries.

By far the most common type of microform found in libraries in this country is roll microfilm in a width of 35 mm. and in lengths up to 100 feet. In Europe, 35 mm. film in strips or rolls and "microfiche" — sheet microfilm in 7.5 by 12.5 or 9 by 12 centimeter sizes — are in common use. In addition to these transparent forms, extensive collections of library materials exist in the form of micro-opaques — Microcards, Microprint, and Microlex.

Many other types and sizes of microtransparencies are widely used in business and industrial applications, such as roll film in 16 mm., 70 mm., and 105 mm. widths; "unitized" 35 mm. film in which individual frames are mounted in Electric Accounting Machine (hereafter referred to as "EAM") cards; and "jacketed" films in which several strips of film are mounted in windows in a transparent jacket to form a sheet of images. With the exception of 16 mm. roll film which is occasionally used, these latter forms are rarely, if ever, found in library collections. Hence, a primary determinant in the choice of reader-printers for testing was whether or not a given machine was capable of printing from the kinds of microforms, transparent or opaque, which are in use in libraries. If, for example, a machine could project 35 mm. film images mounted in EAM cards but had no provision for handling film in roll form, it was excluded from consideration. All machines which were limited to 16 mm., 70 mm., or 105 mm. roll film were also excluded. A number of widely advertised reader-printers thus failed to qualify for consideration in the present study. A brief description of the machines that were excluded and the reasons why they failed to qualify are given in Chapter 13.

Beyond the mere testing of the machines themselves, another purpose of the reader-printer study was to try to establish and present a general outline of the principles involved in the production of enlarged copies from microforms in relation to the particular problems and needs of libraries. In addition to analyses and critiques of particular machines, attention therefore has been given to an analysis of the advantages and disadvantages of different types of reader-printers and of the different processes employed in the machines which were studied.

Libraries have a great and ever-increasing need to be able to produce enlarged copies from microforms in their collections with rapidity, efficiency, and economy. Unfortunately, most of the reader-printers tested fall considerably short of meeting this need. Nonetheless, it is hoped that the facts presented herein will be useful to librarians in the choice of a reader-printer, and that a summation of the inadequacies of presently available equipment may stimulate the development and production of better machines in the future.

William R. Hawken

Berkeley, California
October, 1962

CONTENTS

EQUIPMENT EMPLOYING OTHER PROCESSES

Chapter

FIGURES

Figure

Figure

1 Introduction

The term "reader-printer" can be defined readily enough, but the importance of the present-day need for efficient reader-printers can only be properly understood in the light of the numerous important developments and changes that have taken place in the world of documentation since the introduction of microforms in the early 1930's. Essentially, a reader-printer is nothing more than a device by means of which the projected image of a microform copy of a document can be read and, at will, reproduced in enlarged form on a piece of paper.

The need for efficient reader-printers exists because of a profound change that has taken place in the physical nature of what we call documents. For centuries the word "document" has connoted the idea of a piece of paper on which something was written, printed, or drawn. Indeed, *Webster's New World Dictionary* defines "document" as "anything printed, written, etc., relied upon to record or prove something." Today, however, documents no longer exist in just this one form but in two — the original piece of paper and/or a micro-image of the content of such a piece of paper.

Thirty years ago a micro-image of a document was a remarkable exception to the traditional notion of what constituted a document — so much so that it took a long legal battle to establish microcopies of documents as prima facie evidence in court. Nowadays microcopies of documents are a commonplace. In the fields of business, industry, and government, microfilm was extensively used in its early days as a means for preserving vast collections of bulky and perishable records, and, at the same time, immensely reducing the storage space and equipment required for their preservation. Today, however, micro-photography is widely used not merely in its "dead record" preservation function but as a highly active intermediate process in numerous "live" applications as well.

In the library world, microfilm has also been extensively used for the preservation of bulky and fragile collections of research materials, particularly newspaper files, but in addition it also functions as a highly important acquisitions tool and a medium for the rapid transmission and wide dissemination of research materials. Whereas formerly the scholar had to travel to wherever needed research materials could be found, microphotography has made it possible for research materials to come to the scholar. Thus, in a great many important ways, micro-images of documents have now come to have equal status with original documents themselves, but the methods by which the content of these two classes of documents can be exploited are markedly different, the most important difference being that the use of micro-images depends upon the availability of highly specialized optical aids for reading.

In the past decade, one factor which has had a marked effect on the ways in which original documents are used has resulted from the development of a number of new processes and appropriate equipment for the rapid reproduction of documents. Innumerable offices and libraries, whether large or small, have photocopiers. Photocopying has become so simple and inexpensive that it is now virtually an indispensable part of countless commonplace activities and systems involving the use of documents. But, if documents are in microform, copies legible with the unaided eye are by no means as easily acquired. The need to be able to produce readable copies from microforms is often as great or even greater than the need to make copies from originals, since originals at least can be read without optical aids. It is this situation — the convenience and utility of photocopies as working documents and the lag between the efficiency of the methods by which documents in original form and documents in microform can be reproduced — that has prompted a number of manufacturers to attempt to develop devices whereby enlarged copies from microforms could be produced as quickly and easily as copies from original documents.

If all documents were of a few commonly used sizes and if all micro-images of documents were on, say, 35 mm. film of a fixed-frame size and filmed at a few standard reduction ratios, the problem of devising an efficient reader-printer would be immensely simpler. This, however, is very far indeed from being the case. The family of microtransparencies alone has grown in three decades to include micro-images on 16 mm. and 35 mm. roll films, both perforated and non-perforated, and on films of 70 mm. and 105 mm. widths as well; "unitized" films in which individual frames are cut from rolls and mounted in various types and sizes of EAM cards; and sheet films which may be 7½ by 12½ cm., 9 by 12 cm., 4 by 6 inches, or 5 by 8 inches in size. Furthermore, there is no reason to suppose that this proliferation of sizes has yet reached a limit.

The situation, especially in regard to the making of enlarged prints, was still further complicated by the appearance of micro-images which were on opaque rather than transparent bases. These include the well-known Microcard which measures 3 by 5 inches; Microlex, which measures 6½ by 8½ inches; and Microprint, which is 6 by 9 inches in size. In addition to these variations in physical type and over-all dimensions, still another extensive set of variables is encountered in the different degrees of reduction and different formats employed in producing the various microforms. Depending upon the particular microform being used and the purpose for which the microcopying is being done, groups of documents of identical size may be filmed at different times and places at reduction ratios which can vary over a wide range.

It is hardly necessary to point out that the existence of so many variables, both between and within the many microforms currently in use, immensely complicates the problem of designing an efficient and versatile reader-printer, and that if such a machine could be built it would be a very costly apparatus. What has actually happened, therefore, is that a number of limited purpose reader-printers have appeared on the market — reader-printers which have been designed to handle only certain types of microforms of certain classes of documents which in themselves are fairly well standardized as to size and which are filmed at reduction ratios which also have become fairly well standardized. Chief among these classes of documents are: (a) office records, which are usually "legal size" (8½ by 14 inches), "letter size" (8½ by 11 inches or smaller), and (b) engineering drawings, usually in sizes which are multiples of an 8½- by 11- or 9- by 12-inch area. In the worlds of business, industry, and government, microforms of these two classes of documents now exist in vast quantities. It is not surprising, therefore, to find that most of the reader-printers on the market today have been designed to meet the reproduction requirements of these particular microforms.

Library materials, however, are by no means so conveniently standardized as to size. Bound volumes may range from sextodecimo or smaller to triple folio. Serial publications may range from pocket size to larger than quarto. Page formats may be rectangular in either a horizontal or vertical format, or may be square. Collections of manuscript materials may exhibit extensive variations in size and shape. In scientific publications, the type size used for footnotes, subscript and superscript numbers, mathematical or chemical formulae, or legends on maps or other finely detailed illustrations may be very small indeed. As a consequence of factors such as these, the reduction ratios employed in filming materials which are so heterogeneous in size and diverse in character will necessarily vary over a wide range. Indeed, in the filming of a single volume, the presence of folding plates may require intermittent changes in the reduction ratio being used. A reader-printer capable of providing the librarian or scholar with enlarged prints from a wide variety of library microforms would of necessity have to be quite a flexible and versatile instrument and hence a costly one.

The present situation with regard to reader-printers may therefore be summarized as follows:

1. We now have two major types of documents — originals and microform copies of originals.

2. Original documents can be read with the unaided eye. Microform copies of documents require optical aids for reading.
3. Original documents can now be readily reproduced in a variety of ways. Microforms can be reproduced easily in enlarged form only if the type, size, shape, reduction ratio, and other characteristics of a given microform happen to fall within the capability limitations of a reader-printer.
4. Office records and engineering drawings, and their microforms, are fairly well standardized, and most reader-printers have been designed to reproduce from these microforms. Neither library materials nor their microforms are at all standardized. As a result, a large percentage of library microforms do not fall within the capability limitations of existing reader-printers.

The performance characteristics, advantages, disadvantages, capabilities, and limitations of what few reader-printers do have any potential for the production of enlarged copies from library microforms are analyzed in the chapters that follow.

2 The Fundamentals of Reader-Printers

Reader-printers function in accordance with certain optical and photographic principles which are relatively simple, well-known, and widely used in ordinary photographic practice. Light must fall on a microform image, and either pass through it or be reflected from its surface through a lens that will magnify the image to readable size. The lens must be capable of being focused in order to bring the magnified image to maximum clarity, and this image must fall on a plane surface where a sheet of a suitable light-sensitive material can be placed. Following the exposure of the sensitized material, the latent image thus formed must be developed by means of some chemical or physical process. At the same time, this developed image must be rendered at least reasonably stable so that it will not be unduly affected by light, heat, or atmospheric conditions.

All of the commonly used methods for producing a photographic enlargement — methods which have been widely used for nearly a century — meet all of these conditions. What, then, are the difficulties that have delayed for so long the development of a good reader-printer for microforms? The answer to this question is to be found in four further problems which the *practical* use of microforms imposes.

The first of these is the requirement that the enlarged print be produced under conditions of ordinary room light such as one would expect to find in a library or an office, instead of in a darkroom. Second, the print must be produced very rapidly. Ideally, it should be produced virtually instantaneously. Long print-processing times such as are usual in ordinary photographic work are much too long for practicability in a reader-printer. Third, the print, however it is produced, must be dry, or at least low enough in moisture content to be used immediately or within a few moments. The long drying times common to ordinary photographic methods of print production are also not practicable in a reader-printer. And fourth, the entire operation must be automated to a degree that will eliminate the need for the knowledge and skills which are usually attendant upon the making of photographic enlargements.

Such a degree of automation has not yet been fully realized in the reader-printers which were tested. While all offer solutions of various kinds and degrees for the first three problems, and while the need for special techniques and skills has been largely eliminated, the economical and efficient use of reader-printers still requires some knowledge on the part of the user. The degree of knowledge and experience required varies with the different types of reader-printers.

The best solution to the first problem — the use of a reader-printer in a brightly lit area — has been to enclose the sensitized material within the body of the machine so that only light from the illumination system of the reader-printer falls on the surface of the sensitized material, and then only when a print is being made. Such machines are classed as "internal projection" reader-printers. A compromise solution to the problem caused by ambient light is offered in machines of the "external projection" class, in which the sensitized material is outside of the machine. This solution consists of a balancing of the essential factors — the speed of the sensitized material and the intensity of the illumination system of the reader-printer vs. the brightness of the surrounding illumination. The speed of the materials chosen must be such that the material can be exposed to room light for a period long enough to make a print without danger of over-all fogging or blackening. At the same time the intensity of the illumination system must be great enough to produce a fully exposed print within the allowable time in which the material is exposed to room light. How much ambient light can be tolerated and for how long will vary with different types of materials. A reduction in the amount of ambient light which will permit the use of higher speed materials at shorter exposures is usually desirable because the slower the material is in its response to ambient light, the slower will its response also be to the light from the illumination system of the reader-printer.

Reader-printers of either the internal projection or external projection type consist basically of a light source; an optical system; a means of positioning microforms between these first two components; a screen upon which the projected image can be viewed, positioned, and focused; a supply of a suitable sensitized material; a method of controlling the length of time the sensitized material is exposed; and some sort of device for processing the exposed print. Given all of these components in a functioning state, one then introduces a microform and immediately encounters the chief problem which the operator, and not the machine, must solve — the choice of a correct exposure interval which will yield a satisfactory print from the particular microform in question. This microform may be a negative microtransparency, a positive microtransparency, or a micro-opaque. The problems connected with exposure determination with each of these types of microforms must now be considered.

The commonest difference among transparent, negative microforms, especially those acquired from different sources, will be in the *background density* of the images. When a negative microfilm is made, the white areas of a page of text record as a tone ranging from gray to black while the black image of the text records as clear, or nearly clear, transparent areas. How black the background tone will be will vary with both the amount of exposure and the degree of development which the film receives. In a photographic laboratory, the index for the making of a correctly exposed print from a microfilm negative, whether the print be a duplicate film or one or more enlarged paper prints, is the degree of blackness or *density* of the background areas. Hence the term "background density." If the print is insufficiently exposed, too little light will pass through the translucent text areas to form a clear, sharp black image. If the print is overexposed, the characters of the text will be heavy and filled, and enough light may by then have passed through the black background to cause an over-all grayish appearance on the print.

Background densities are expressed in a logarithmic scale usually comprising a range from 0.00 to 3.00, 0.00 representing the perfect, unimpeded transmission of light and 3.00 representing virtually total opacity. In applications where it is necessary, background density can be read on an instrument called a densitometer, by means of which the light transmitting characteristics of a given background area can be measured and expressed within the 0.00 to 3.00 range. Negative microfilms of average subjects which will yield good quality prints should have background densities which will fall roughly within the 1.00 to 2.00 range. If the background density of a negative falls below 1.00, the best print that can be obtained under optimum conditions is usually grayish and lacking in contrast. While it may be clear and fairly sharply defined, the lack of contrast makes legibility difficult. Negatives which exceed a background density of 2.00 often exhibit veiled and broken lines since the exposure required to produce such a density is usually excessive and causes the background to encroach on the text areas.

Thus, when making enlarged prints with most of the reader-printers tested, the choice of an exposure time that will yield a satisfactory print will depend on the background density of the negative being printed, but since densitometric readings for the predetermination of the correct exposure will not be available to the user, some guesswork and trial-and-error experiments will be involved, and some waste of materials will inevitably ensue. Experience, in this case, is the best teacher. It is easy to see that if the projected image is low in contrast and very bright on the reader screen, a short exposure will be required, and that if, on the other hand, the background is quite black and the lines of the text dim and veiled, a longer exposure will be required. How short or how long the exposure should be is still guesswork, but it can, in the light of previous experience, become at least an informed guess.

The situation in printing from positive microtransparencies is the opposite, and in some ways, even more difficult. While one can learn to estimate exposures on the basis of the appearance of the background density of a negative when this background occupies most of the screen area, estimates of the correct exposure for the reproduction of tiny line densities against a clear background are more difficult. Underexposed prints from positive transparencies of first-rate quality yield fuzzy white letters against a mealy, grayish background. Overexposed prints yield veiled, broken letters against a heavy gray or black background. The situation is further complicated by the fact that the positive transparency has been produced from a negative transparency, and may or may not have been properly exposed and processed to begin with. If such is the case, the problem of correct exposure determination becomes increasingly difficult, and waste will be proportionately higher.

The problem of exposure determination is further complicated by changes in the degree of magnification. In the case of external projection reader-printers, which are really only photographic enlargers modified and adapted to be reader-printers, the lens-to-subject distance, which also controls the size of the projected image, affects exposure in proportion to this distance. If, for the projection of a negative of a given background density, the magnification needed for legibility is low, and therefore the lens-to-subject distance quite short, the image will be relatively bright and the required exposure relatively short. But if, on the other hand, from a negative of equal background density, the magnification must, in the interests of legibility, be high, the projected image will be fainter and the exposure much longer. Again, in the absence of instruments and knowledge which can measure and interpret these factors, correct exposure determination will be nothing more than guesswork with waste materials as the inevitable concomitant.

In theory, the making of enlarged prints from micro-opaques is somewhat simpler because with only rare exceptions, micro-opaque images are positive and are printed on white paper stocks which are quite uniform and consistent in their ability to reflect light. The strength of the image, however, will depend on the strength, clarity, and contrast of the original and the excellence of the micro-opaque reproduction. If the micro-opaque image itself tends to be heavy, small spaces within and between letters will be narrower. If a print from such an image is also slightly overexposed, these tiny spaces may fill entirely, which may cause a serious loss in legibility. On the other hand, if the micro-opaque image tends to be weak or faint, the lines of the text itself may be quite thin, or may even show some degree of vignetting (fading of the image into the white background). If a print from an image of this kind is the least bit underexposed, faint or vignetted lines may not reproduce at all and legibility will be seriously impaired. Therefore, despite a greater degree of uniformity of background tone, the exposures required for micro-opaques can be even more critical than from micro-transparencies.

Thus, while there are now several devices which are capable of providing an enlarged print from a microform with unparalleled rapidity, the user is still faced with certain problems. All is not yet as easy nor as automatic as one could wish it to be. In reader-printers, the age in which "you push the button and the machine does the rest" has not quite arrived. And until it does, knowledge of how to make the best available machines work efficiently and economically is still necessary.

3 Processes for Rapid Print Production

The solution to the problem of rapidly producing an enlarged print of the image projected on the screen of a microform reading device was brought about through the development of a number of new processes, some of which departed radically from the time-honored silver halide system of photography. The first of these to consider is an electrolytic process developed by the Minnesota Mining and Manufacturing Company. This process was first introduced in 1957 and is used in all of the reader-printers marketed by that company, under its trade name of "Filmac." (Models 100, 200-R, and 300 are described in subsequent chapters.)

In this electrolytic process, the sensitized material consists of three layers: a paper base, a thin layer of a metal foil such as aluminum, and, on top of this, a coating of zinc oxide in a resin binder. This zinc oxide coating provides a photoconductive layer which in the dark acts as an insulator — i.e., it has high electrical resistance. But the action of light during exposure lowers the resistance in those areas where light strikes the surface. Thus, a latent image is formed in terms of differences in electrical resistance, the image areas having now become electrically conductive through the action of light. If the exposed sheet is then placed very briefly in contact with a suitable electroplating solution and a d.c. electric potential applied, current can flow between the solution and the aluminum-foil layer. This causes metal ions in the solution to deposit or "plate out" on the zinc oxide surface in the image areas to form a visible metallic image. This processing step in which electrolytic formation of the image occurs is accomplished with great simplicity and rapidity, requiring, as it does, nothing more than drawing the zinc oxide surface over an ordinary cellulose sponge soaked with the solution. The processing of an 8½- by 11-inch print requires no more than about 4½ seconds, and since the surface of the print is only barely moistened during processing, the print can be considered, for all practical purposes, as dry.

The strength or line density of the image can be controlled both through variations in the exposure and variations in the processing. Exposure control is simply a matter of increasing or decreasing the length of time light falls on the sensitized material. Processing control is effected by means of a rheostat which regulates the intensity of the electric current which passes between the electrolyte and the aluminum-foil layer. The higher the intensity of this current, the greater is the deposition of image-forming components on the zinc oxide surface. The presence of these two sets of controls is not, however, an indication that exposure and processing are critical matters which require skillful manipulation on the part of the operator. Actually, the electrolytic process possesses remarkable latitude. With most microfilms, satisfactory prints can be made over a wide range of exposure and processing settings and different combinations of settings. While the prints will range from light to dark, clarity of the image is not affected.

Prints made by the electrolytic process do not have as much contrast as prints made by conventional silver halide photocopy processes. The deepest tone is never a solid black. This very lack of contrast, however, is a considerable advantage when reproducing from negative microtransparencies which contain continuous-tone illustrations.

On the basis of what is publicly known about the chemistry of the electrolytic process employed in the Filmac line of reader-printers, the prints should have a high degree of stability.

A second process which also provides a rapidly produced print which is nearly dry is the stabilization process (exemplified in later chapters by the Documat Reader-Printers, the Rollacopy and the Micromate, and the Universel). Although it has been in use for several years, recent developments in the applicable materials and equipment have reached a point where this process is now of considerable importance in the entire photocopy field. It is now being used in office copying machines, book copiers, devices for the rapid reproduction of engineering drawings from micro-images, and in three of the reader-printers which were tested.

The fundamental difference between conventional and stabilization processing lies in the different chemical treatment of the exposed and developed silver halide image. To form a permanent, or even semipermanent, image by conventional processing techniques, the silver halides which were not used in the formation of the developed image, and which, if allowed to remain in the print, will rapidly turn dark on exposure to light, are dissolved out of the paper by means of a "fixing bath" — the well-known "hypo." Following this fixation step, the hypo, now laden with silver compounds, must be removed from the paper by prolonged washing.

In the stabilization process, the unused silver halides are not removed from the print. Instead, they are chemically converted into substances which are relatively inert and which are not readily affected by the subsequent action of light, heat, or atmospheric conditions. Thus, the classical four-bath method — developing, rinsing, fixing, and washing — which might take upward of an hour, is reduced to two steps, development and stabilization, which can be accomplished in seconds.

Two recent improvements in the stabilization process which have aided in bringing it into prominence have been the incorporation of the developing agent in the light-sensitive coating of the paper itself and the manufacture of compact, efficient processing devices, similar in appearance to diffusion-transfer-reversal processors, for the rapid processing of exposed prints. By incorporating the developing agent in the paper emulsion instead of having it in the developing solution, chemical life is greatly extended, since deterioration of solution strength because of aerial oxidation of the developing agent has thus been eliminated. Stabilization processors consist of two trays — one containing a highly alkaline activator and the other the stabilizing solution — and a series of power-driven rollers which advance the exposed print through the solutions and remove most of the moisture as the print comes out of the machine. The combination of a developing agent within the paper coating with a suitable activator and stabilizer makes it possible for the processing to be very rapid indeed. For example, in the Polymicro processor used with the Rollacopy and Micromate (see Chapter 8), the leading edge of an exposed print emerges from the machine just five seconds after entry.

In copying from original documents, the first copy is negative, and if a positive copy is needed the negative must then be recopied. The production of positive copies is therefore a two-stage process rather than a one-stage process as is the case with diffusion-transfer-reversal or Verifax. The negative, however, can be retained as a master and used for the printing of additional positives as needed.

Unlike most other document-reproduction processes, sensitized materials of several degrees of contrast are available for use with the stabilization process. This can be a distinct advantage in cases where high contrast tends to make exposures quite critical or where any unevenness in the illumination system of the copying or projecting device becomes exaggerated by excessive contrast to the point of interfering with legibility. Lower contrast materials are also beneficial in copying continuous-tone illustrations.

A disadvantage, at least from the standpoint of the librarian or archivist, lies in the fact that stabilized copies, by the nature of the process, are of doubtful permanence. Depending upon the conditions of light, heat, and humidity under which they are stored, they will keep for a period of months or for many years without appreciable change in their appearance, but they cannot be considered to possess what is usually called "archival permanence."

A third process which is being used in certain reader-printers designed for the reproduction of engineering drawing is xerography.

None of these reader-printers, however, could be considered as suitable for the reproduction of library microforms.

A fourth process which is used in one microform enlarging device (the Microcard Copier Type I, Chapter 10) is the well-known diffusion-transfer-reversal process, which is widely used in office copying machines. In this process, a negative sheet is first exposed and then placed in contact with a positive receiving sheet. The two sheets are then passed through a simple processing device containing a developing solution. During this processing, which takes but a few seconds, both a negative, reverse-reading image and a right-reading positive image are produced. When the sheets have emerged from the machine they are allowed to remain in contact for a few seconds and then separated.

DTR prints exhibit strong contrast. From a good original the text is a well-defined black image against a white background. Unfortunately, high contrast tends to make exposures quite critical, which can often result in wasted materials from trial-and-error attempts to obtain an exposure which will yield a fully legible copy of the desired document.

Like stabilization-process prints, DTR prints are of doubtful permanence unless they have been washed after processing.

4 The Filmac 100

General description

The Filmac Model 100 reader-printer first appeared on the market in 1958. Minor improvements have been made in the machine since then, but the basic design and operating principles remain unchanged. The extreme simplicity of the operation of this device comes about through the use of the electrolytic process for print production described in Chapter 3.

The unit consists of a metal housing which contains an illumination system, an optical system, a viewing screen, a film-transport system, a system for holding and transporting the sensitized material, and a processing section for electrolytic development of the latent image. Both the intensity of the current which controls the deposition of image-forming components and the duration of the exposure are controlled by means of conveniently located knobs.

This unit can be used for printing from 16 mm. and 35 mm. microfilm and from microfiche. Once basic exposures have been established, and the machine loaded with paper and activator, printing requires nothing more than locating and positioning the desired frame and pressing the "print" button. In a few seconds, depending on the duration of the exposure, the finished print emerges at the top of the unit where it can be torn off.

Specifications

Manufacturer: Minnesota Mining and Manufacturing Company.

Where manufactured: United States.

Process employed: Electrolytic.

Measurements: Width—16 inches. Depth of base—16 inches. Depth of top—19 inches. Height—24½ inches. Weight—80 pounds.

Size of viewing screen: 7 by 8¼ inches.

Size of print: 8½ by 11 inches.

Size of image on print: 7 by 8¼ inches.

Size of roll stock microfilm copy paper: 8½ inches by 298 feet.

Cost per roll: $25.71 (in lots of four rolls).

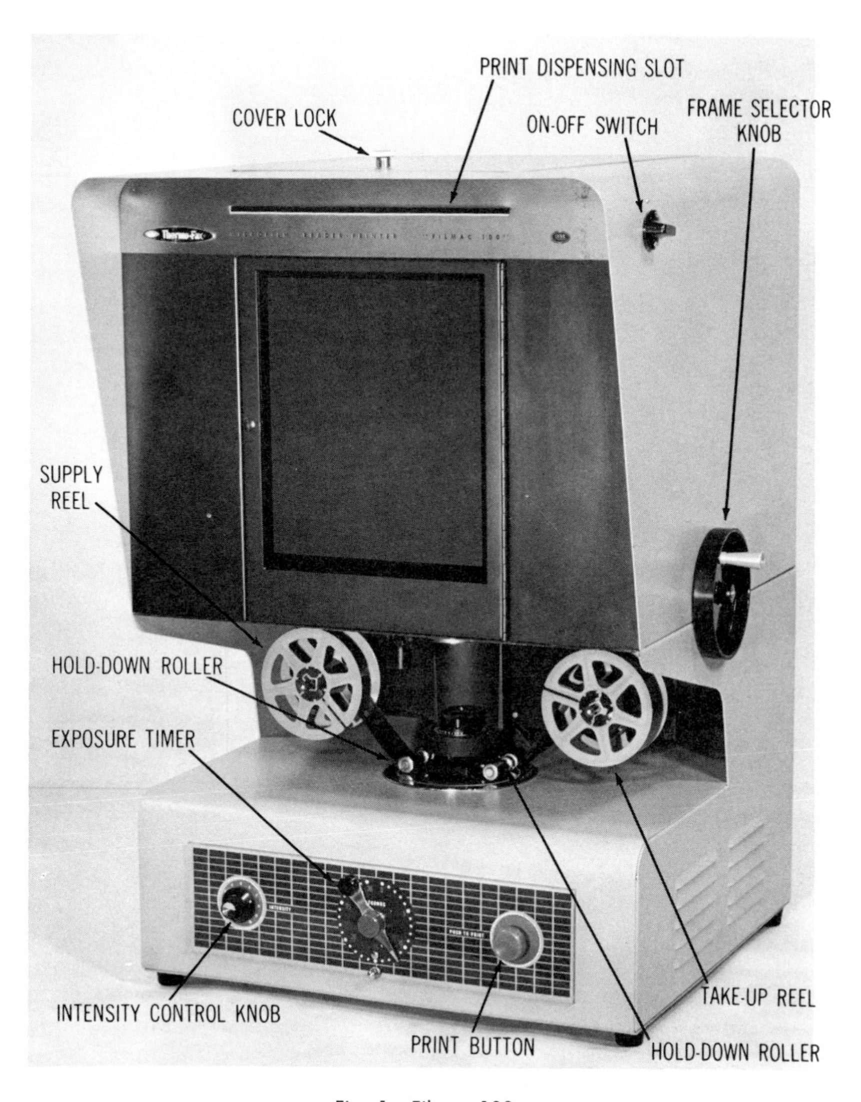

Fig. 1. Filmac 100.

Lenses available:

Focal Length	Magnification
50 mm.	7X
40 mm.	9X
30 mm.	13X
22.4 mm.	19X
16.3 mm.	26X

Focusing method: Helical mounts.

Power requirements: 115 volts; 60 cycles; 3 amperes.

Electrical components: Paper drive motor; fan motor; 150-watt, 20-volt projection lamp; transformer; fuse.

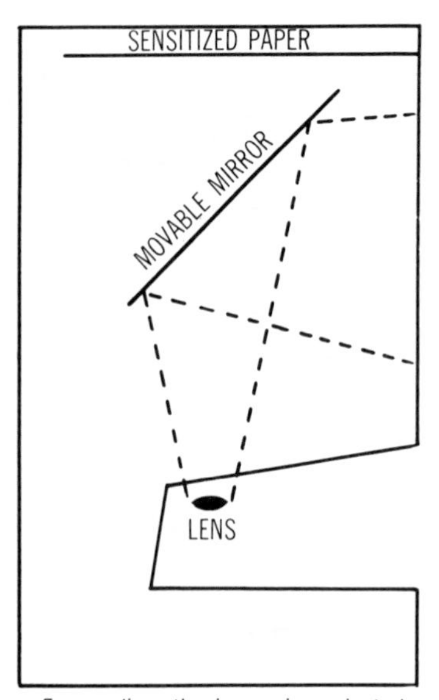

For reading, the image is projected upward to a movable mirror which reflects the image forward to the viewing screen.

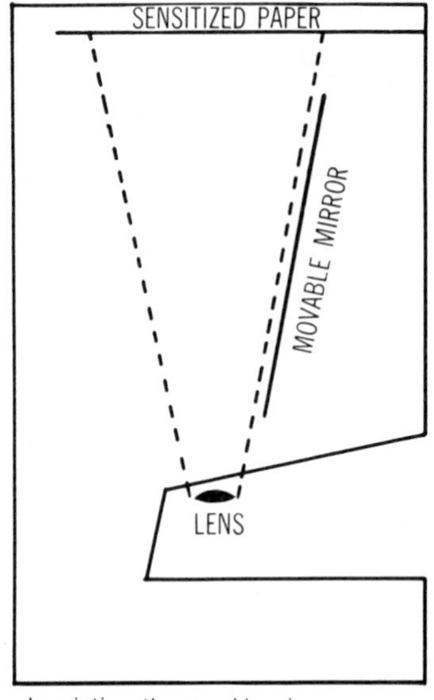

In printing, the movable mirror moves out of the path of the projected image so that it can fall on the surface of the sensitized material.

Fig. 2. Schematic diagram of the mirror system of the Filmac 100.

To replace lamp: A small door at the rear of the machine provides access to the projection lamp. The lamp is mounted on a hinged base which is held in a vertical position by a small catch. By turning this catch to the right, the base can be tilted into a horizontal position facing the access door. The lamp can then be readily removed and replaced and the base returned to its vertical position.

Construction: Cast metal and sheet metal frame and housing; plastic activator tray; rubber-covered rollers on stainless steel shafts.

Film-transport assembly: Capacity—100-foot rolls of 16 mm. or 35 mm. microfilm. Spindles—2:1 ratio on 1⅞-inch radius. Flats—Lower glass flat fixed. Upper glass flat hinged. Pressure between flats maintained by gravity. Both flats removable for cleaning. Image position — Entire film-transport assembly can be rotated a full 360 degrees and can be moved from side to side or front to back by means of traverse knobs.

Maintenance: Each morning, or after any extended period when the machine has not been in use, the paper drive rollers should be cleaned with a damp cloth. Periodically, the sponge and activator tray should be removed and cleaned. The sponge should be thoroughly washed in clear warm water only. Should the sponge become dry, both the sponge and activator tray should be removed and cleaned. The manufacturer recommends that the mirror, the upper and lower glass flats, and the viewing screen be gently cleaned with a dampened soft sponge and soap, rinsed with a soft sponge dampened in clear water, and dried with a lint-free cloth or chamois. Dust should be removed from the lenses by means of a camel's-hair brush and the lenses should occasionally be cleaned very gently with lens tissue.

Cost of machine: $629 with one lens.

Cost of additional lenses: $66.50 each.

Warranty: Six-month warranty covering repair or replacement of defective parts. Following the expiration of the warranty, a service contract for the maintenance of the machine is available at a minimum cost of $50.00 per year.

Operation

Before printing can be done, the activator tray must be filled to the proper level, and the machine must be loaded with a roll of microfilm copy paper.

The activator tray is a small plastic tray containing a cellulose sponge (Figure 3). The rear and bottom sides of the tray are lined with a metal conducting plate connected to a wire lead which plugs into a jack. This circuit provides the current employed in the electrolytic development of the print. With the tray in place, activator is poured from a dispensing bottle over the sponge (Figure 4) until the sponge is completely soaked from end to end, and with enough excess to fill the bottom of the tray to a depth of about ⅛ inch. Care must be taken in soaking the sponge and filling the tray so that no activator is spilled into the machine. Also, since the activator tends to stain clothing, the dispensing bottle should be firmly capped and kept in a place where there will be no danger of its being spilled accidentally. In the course of printing, the level of the activator in the tray should be checked from time to time and brought up to the required level as needed. If prints begin to show streaks, this is an indication that more activator is needed.

The paper-tracking system consists of a pair of spring-loaded spindles at the rear of the machine, a pair of rubber-covered power-driven rollers at the front, and a cut-off bar. To load a roll of paper into the machine, the "on-off" switch is placed in the "off" position. This separates the two rubber-covered drive rollers. The hinged

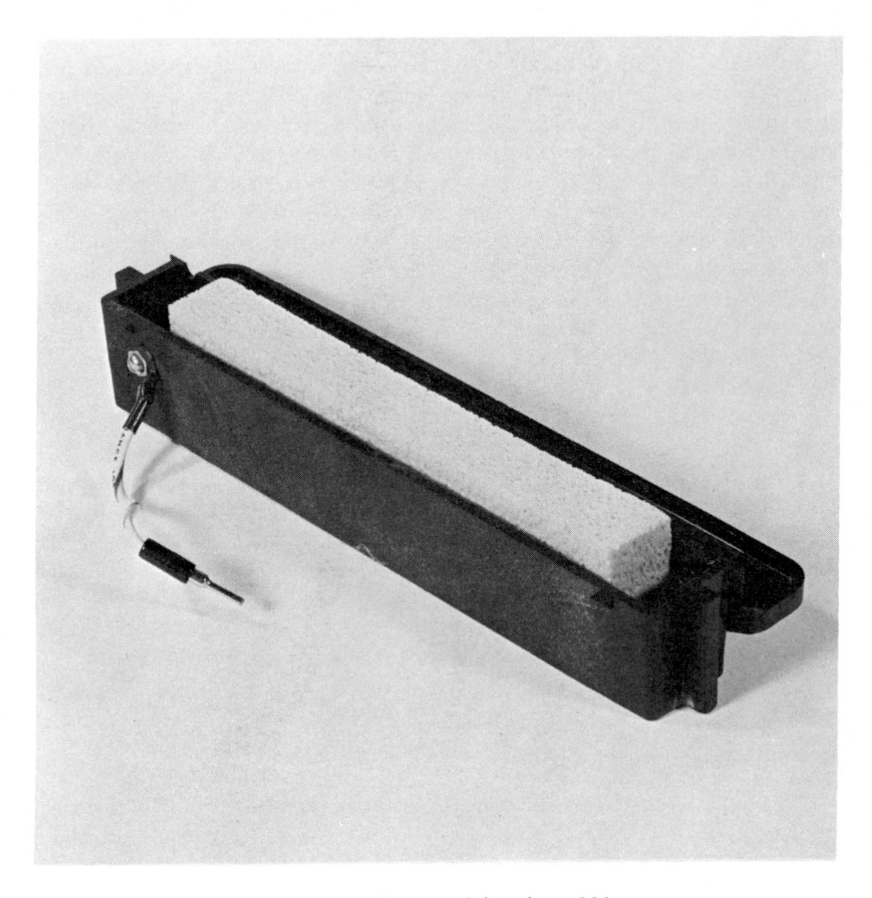

Fig. 3. Activator tray of the Filmac 100.

cover of the machine is then lifted and folded back. The roll of paper is placed between the spindles so that when the leading edge of the paper is brought up and over the top of the machine the sensitized (inside) surface will be face down (Figure 5). The leading edge of the paper is then folded to form a "V" and the point of the "V" drawn over the activator tray and inserted between the drive rollers (Figure 6). The cover of the machine is then closed, and two feet of paper drawn forward. The "on-off" switch is then turned to the "on" position to lock the paper advance rollers in position and the two-foot leader torn off against the cut-off bar.

The film-transport assembly (Figure 7) consists first of all of two spindles which, by means of a set of nylon gears and a shaft, are connected to a film-advance knob called the "frame selector" which is located at the right side of the machine. Between the spindles and the lens there are two "hold-down" rollers which are spring-loaded and can be snapped to an "up" position when film is being threaded into the machine, and then snapped into a "down" position to hold the film for tracking between a pair of glass flats which hold the film in an even plane for viewing and printing. The lower glass flat is a circular disk called a "window disk" mounted in a metal frame. It is held in place by a hole which fits in place over a pin and can be removed when necessary by lifting it off the pin and sliding it forward. The upper glass flat is hinged and "floating" and can be raised when film is being threaded into the machine.

Fig. 4. Filling the activator tray.

Thus, to load a reel of film into the machine, the supply reel is placed on one spindle with the emulsion side of the film facing up, the hold-down rollers are snapped into the "up" position, the film is tracked between the two glass flats and threaded into the take-up reel and the hold-down rollers snapped back into the "down" position (Figure 1). With the projection lamp turned on, the desired image is located by turning the frame selector knob and is positioned for printing by operating the traverse knobs. The entire film-transport assembly can be rotated a full 360 degrees.

Control of the size of the image on the reader screen is accomplished through the use of different lenses which provide magnifications of 7, 9, 13, 19, and 26 diameters. The arm which holds the lenses in position over the film is a metal casting having a circular hole which has tapered sides. The lenses are screwed into collars which have tapered sides that match the angle of the taper of the lens holder. Changing lenses involves nothing more than lifting out one lens and collar and replacing it with another. All the lenses are mounted in barrels which have helical focusing mounts. The condensing lenses, however, do not provide an even field of illumination for all five lenses. When the 13-, 19-, or 26-diameter lenses are

Fig. 5. Loading a roll of microfilm copy paper.

Fig. 6. Threading the paper through the drive rollers.

being used, no change in the condenser lenses is needed, but accessory condenser lenses must be used when the 7X or 9X lenses are used.

To even the field of illumination for a magnification of 7X, the circular metal ring which holds the lower glass flat ("window disk") must be removed by lifting the hold-down rollers, raising the ring off the pin which holds it in place, and sliding it forward. Access may then be had to the upper condenser lens which is held in place by three clips, one of which is fastened by a screw. By re-

Fig. 7. Film-transport assembly showing hold-down rollers in "up" position for loading.

moving the screw and clip, the upper condenser lens can then be lifted out. The lower glass flat is then lifted out of its metal ring and replaced with a special convex condensing lens. The ring is then reinserted and dropped into position over the retaining pin.

To even the field of illumination for a magnification of 9X, the metal ring and lower glass flat are removed but the upper condenser lens is not. The lower glass flat in this case is replaced with a special concave condensing lens and the ring placed back in position.

The lightness or darkness of the print can be controlled by two methods (Figure 1). The first of these is by means of an automatic electric timing device of the "set" variety which has a scale divided in seconds over a range of from 1 to 30. Should it be necessary, in printing from an exceptionally dense negative, to use an exposure longer than thirty seconds, the pointer on the exposure dial can be turned backward during the course of the exposure to increase the total exposure time.

The second method for controlling the strength of the image is by means of an "intensity" knob which does not control the intensity of the light source, as one might suppose, but controls instead the amount of current flowing through the electrolyte to the metallic-foil layer of the sensitized material. It thus controls the extent of the deposition of the image-forming materials.

Two modified versions of the Filmac 100 are offered by the manufacturer. The first of these, which was recently announced, is known as the Filmac 100M and differs from the Filmac 100 only in that the film advance is motorized. The variable speed control on the motor permits very slow advancement of the film or, when rewinding, a high speed which will rewind a 100-foot roll in 35 seconds. The suggested retail price of the Filmac 100M is $879 with one lens. The standard Filmac 100 can be converted to a 100M for a cost of approximately $250.

The second modified version is known as the Filmac 100C and is a coin-in-the-slot machine. The coin-operating attachment can be set to operate at predetermined copy charges of 15, 20, or 25 cents. No list price for this unit has been announced.

The Filmac 100C is not the first coin-in-the-slot Filmac reader-printer. The firm of Bodine, Bryson and Rolling, Inc., of Birmingham, Alabama, equipped a Filmac 100 with a coin-in-the-slot attachment for the public library in Anniston, Alabama. This unit operates on 25-cent pieces. For the benefit of others who might be interested, the company is prepared to furnish all necessary parts for this modification for $75.00, or can arrange for complete installation through any local Thermofax sales office for a total cost of $105. The Berkeley Public Library in Berkeley, California, also has had a Filmac 100 equipped with a coin-in-the-slot attachment which works on 10-cent pieces.

Analysis

On the whole, the Filmac 100 is a well-engineered, well-designed, and well-constructed reader-printer. Certain problems, however, were encountered, some of which are minor and could be remedied relatively easily, and others, particularly in printing from library microforms, which are major, and severely limit the utility of the machine as a reproduction device for library use.

In printing from negative microfilms of average density and contrast, the grayishness of the image did not impair legibility. Even though the image was not black it was nevertheless quite sharply defined against its background. In printing from positive microfilms, however, the lack of contrast between the text and the dark gray background produced a much less satisfactory result. Furthermore, even when fresh activator was used and maintained at the proper level, the gray background was uneven in tone and streaked. While in most cases legible prints could be obtained, many were legible only with difficulty. The best prints obtainable were substantially inferior to the clear, contrasty, white-on-black prints obtainable with most other photocopy processes.

Another problem with the materials was encountered in filing and storing prints. Groups of prints stored in folders in a file drawer exhibited a decided tendency to curl. This is in part due to the fact that the microfilm copy paper has coatings on one side and in part to the fact that the paper is quite heavy. Seventy sheets of the microfilm copy paper weigh a pound, whereas 70 sheets of a 20-pound bond paper weigh 11½ ounces and 70 sheets of sulfite canary bond such as is commonly used for carbon copies weigh but 9 ounces. The microfilm copy paper thus weighs from half again to almost twice as much as the papers ordinarily used for office records.

The lower glass flat is readily removed for cleaning, but the upper flat is more difficult to remove. The spring steel arms which support the upper flat on either side must be spread to free the flat for removal. This is most easily done by loosening the small screws at the rear end of each arm. If, however, either of the screws is loosened too much and falls out, replacing it can be difficult because of its relatively inaccessible position and lack of working room. A much more difficult mechanical operation, however, is the removal and replacement of the clip which holds the upper condenser lens in place. This condenser must be removed when the 7X lens is used and replaced when changing to a lens of any other magnification. The clip is located at the rear of the condenser where accessibility is extremely poor. Considerable care and dexterity are required to remove and replace it, and there is always the hazard that the slightest clumsy move may cause the clip, the screw, or both, to drop out of reach into the base of the machine.

The locating pin which holds the lower glass flat in place projects above the surface of the metal ring which encloses it. This is no hazard when roll microfilm is being read, but when sheet microfilm is being read, the sheets may move over this pin and become scratched. The pin should be filed down so it is flush with the surface of the metal ring.

By far the most serious drawbacks encountered in the use of the Filmac 100 for the reproduction of library microforms were caused by the limited size of the screen and inadequate control over the image size imposed by the fixed magnification ratios of the available lenses. The Filmac 100 was designed primarily for the reproduction of microfilms of office records and the size of the image, the size of the print, and the magnification ratios of the lenses supplied are all tailored to meet this need. The commonest sizes of office records in general use are 8½ by 11 inches and 8½ by 14 inches. Library materials, however, are by no means so standardized in size. Furthermore, the filming formats and reduction ratios employed in the automatic or semiautomatic equipment used in the filming of most office records also tend to be much more standardized than is the case in the filming of library materials. Indeed, in the filming of library materials, it is by no means uncommon to have on a single strip of film a series of articles, each from a journal of a different size, and each filmed at a different reduction ratio. A common format used in the filming of library materials is the full frame of 35 mm. non-perforated microfilm which measures 1¼ by 1¾ inches. A folding plate or table, let us say, filmed on a frame of these dimensions, could only be reproduced on the Filmac 100 in sections. Using magnifications of 7X or 9X, four prints would be required. Eight prints would be required with the 13X lens, and, with the 19X lens, 15 prints.

In Table 1 is shown the manufacturer's figures on several common document sizes and the size of the longest dimension of the image on an 8½- by 11-inch print when certain of the more common reduction ratios are used in conjunction with the lenses supplied with the Filmac 100. Table 2 shows in the left-hand column the dimensions of the area which can be filmed on a full frame of 35 mm. non-perforated film at reduction ratios ranging from 7 to 20.

TABLE 1

Document Size in Inches	Reduction Ratio	Magnification	Copy Size (Larger Dimension —in Inches)	Percent Blow-Back
3¼ x 4⅞	1:24	26X	5⅜	111
3¼ x 4⅞	1:30	26X	4 5/16	89
3¼ x 4⅞	1:40	26X	3¼	67
3½ x 8½	1:24	19X	6⅝	78
3½ x 8½	1:30	26X	7½	89
3½ x 8½	1:40	26X	5⅝	67
7 x10	1:10	9X	8 7/16*	95
8½ x11	1:10	9X	8 7/16*	95
8½ x11	1:16	13X	8 7/16*	82
8½ x11	1:20	13X	7¼	65
8½ x11	1:24	19X	8 7/16*	78
8½ x11	1:30	19X	6⅞	63
8½ x11	1:40	26X	7⅜	67
8½ x14	1:12	7X	8¼	58
8½ x14	1:16	9X	8¼	56
8½ x14	1:20	13X	8 7/16*	65
8½ x14	1:24	13X	7⅝	55
8½ x14	1:30	19X	8 7/16*	63
8½ x14	1:40	19X	6⅝	47
10 x13	1:12	7X	. . .	58
10 x13	1:16	9X	7¾	59
11 x14	1:16	9X	8¼	59
11 x14	1:20	13X	8 7/16*	65
11 x14	1:24	13X	7⅝	55
11 x14	1:30	19X	8 7/16*	63
11 x14	1:40	19X	6⅝	47
11 x17	1:16	7X	8 7/16*	44
11 x17	1:16	9X	8 7/16*	59
11 x17	1:20	9X	8⅛	48
11 x17	1:24	13X	8 7/16*	55
11 x17	1:30	13X	7⅜	44
11 x17	1:40	19X	8	47
17 x22	1:20	9X	8 7/16*	48
17 x22	1:24	9X	8 7/16*	40
15½ x23	1:24	9X	8 7/16*	40

*Copy does not cover 100 percent of original document; but coverage is sufficiently high to be satisfactory in most cases.

TABLE 2

Reduction Ratio	Dimensions in Inches of Area Microfilmed on Full 1¼- by 1¾-inch Frame, Non-Perforated 35 mm. Film (Recordak MRD-2 Camera)	Dimensions in Inches of Area which can be Reproduced on a Single 7- by 8¼-inch print			
		7X Lens	9X Lens	13X Lens	19X Lens
7	8.75 x 12.25	7.0 x 8.25	5.44 x 6.42	3.77 x 4.44	2.58 x 3.04
8	10.0 x 14.0	8.0 x 9.43	6.22 x 7.33	4.31 x 5.08	2.94 x 3.47
9	11.25 x 15.75	9.0 x 10.61	7.0 x 8.25	4.85 x 5.71	3.31 x 3.9
10	12.5 x 17.5	10.0 x 11.79	7.77 x 9.16	5.38 x 6.35	3.68 x 4.34
11	13.75 x 19.25	11.0 x 12.96	8.55 x 10.08	5.92 x 6.98	4.05 x 4.78
12	15.0 x 21.0	12.0 x 14.14	9.33 x 11.0	6.46 x 7.62	4.42 x 5.21
13	16.25 x 22.75	13.0 x 15.32	10.11 x 11.92	7.0 x 8.25	4.79 x 5.64
14	17.5 x 24.5	14.0 x 16.5	10.88 x 12.83	7.54 x 8.88	5.16 x 6.08
15	18.75 x 26.25	15.0 x 17.68	11.66 x 13.75	8.08 x 9.52	5.53 x 6.51
16	20.0 x 28.0	16.0 x 18.86	12.44 x 14.66	8.62 x 10.15	5.89 x 6.95
17	21.25 x 29.75	17.0 x 20.03	13.22 x 15.58	9.15 x 10.79	6.26 x 7.38
18	22.5 x 31.5	18.0 x 21.21	14.00 x 16.5	9.69 x 11.42	6.63 x 7.82
19	23.75 x 33.25	19.0 x 22.39	14.77 x 17.42	10.23 x 12.06	7.0 x 8.25
20	25.0 x 35.0	20.0 x 23.57	15.55 x 18.33	10.77 x 12.69	7.37 x 8.68

The right-hand columns show how little of this area can be reproduced on a single print made with the 7X, 9X, 13X, or 19X lenses. Expressed in percentages, the 7X lens reproduces 54 percent of the area of a full frame, the 9X lens 32.6 percent, the 13X lens 15.7 percent, and the 19X lens only 7.3 percent.

Table 3 shows the reduction ratio which must be employed in the filming of four typical serials if the entire text area of a single page is to be reproduced on a single print when using any one of four Filmac lenses. If the reduction ratio is higher than that shown, the image will be correspondingly smaller in size on the print, and this may affect legibility. If, on the other hand, the reduction is lower than that shown for any lens, sectional printing will be required.

TABLE 3

Subject	Text Dimensions in Inches (Single Page)	Reduction Ratio Required in Filming to Permit Reproduction of One Page on One Print			
		7X Lens	9X Lens	13X Lens	19X Lens
Unesco Bulletin For Libraries	4⅝ x 7⅞	7	9	13	19
College and Research Libraries	5 3/16 x 8	7	9	13	19
Photo Science and Technique	6⅞ x 9⅜	8.5	10.5	15.5	22.5
American Documentation	6¾ x 9¼	8	10.5	15	22

Since journals of the sizes shown can be, and frequently are, filmed at a reduction ratio of ten times, it will be seen from this table that if the 7X lens is used, all four journal pages can be reproduced on a single print but all will be reduced somewhat in size. If the 9X lens is used, the two smaller journals can be reproduced on a single print at a slight reduction in size but the larger two will require two prints each to reproduce the entire text. If either the 13X or 19X lens is used, no page can be reproduced on a single print and increasingly large numbers of sectional prints will be required as the magnification is increased.

Summary

When the Filmac 100 is used for the reproduction of the types and sizes of microforms for which it was designed, it is capable of turning in a fairly satisfactory performance. With the exception of the difficulties involved in changing condensers for use with the 7X lens and changing back again, the machine is well designed in terms of operator convenience. While the paper presently available for use in the Filmac 100 is heavy and tends to curl and sag when filed vertically, this drawback has to be weighed against the ease and speed with which prints can be produced, even in the hands of a tyro. The exceptional exposure latitude possessed by the electrolytic process goes a long way toward the elimination of the waste from trial-and-error exposure determinations which is common to several other photocopying processes. The Filmac 100 comes closer than any other machine to the ideal of "you push the button and the machine does the rest." Exposure latitude and automation are factors which are highly desirable in a reader-printer.

But unfortunately for the librarian or scholar, this machine was never designed in the first place with his needs in mind. As a result, it may succeed admirably in the reproduction of office records but fail egregiously as a device for the reproduction of numerous library microforms.

5 | The Filmac 200-R

General description

The first model Filmac reader-printer of the larger size, the Model 200, was designed for viewing and for making 18- by 24-inch prints of microfilm frames of engineering drawings mounted in EAM cards. The Model 200-R is a modification of this original unit which permits microfilm in roll form to be viewed or printed, in addition to film in EAM cards. Prints are produced by the electrolytic process.

Specifications

Manufacturer: Minnesota Mining and Manufacturing Company.

Fig. 8. Filmac 200-R.

Where manufactured: United States.

Process employed: Electrolytic.

Measurements: Width—31 inches. Depth—36 inches. Height—32 inches. Weight—300 pounds.

Size of viewing screen: 18 by 24 inches.

Size of print: 18 by 26 inches.

Size of image on print: 17½ by 24 inches.

Size of roll stock microfilm copy paper: 18 inches by 237 feet.

Cost per roll: $28.06 (in lots of four rolls).

Lens: Aperture—f6.3. Focal length—65 mm. Magnification—15X (fixed).

Focusing method: Helical mount.

Power requirements: 110 volts; 60 cycles; 6 amperes.

Electrical components: Paper advance motor; fan motor; mirror actuating motor; projection lamp; fuse.

To replace lamp: Remove the shield over the lamp house by pulling straight up. Remove the lamp by turning counter-clockwise and pulling up. Replace the lamp and lamp-house shield by reversing this procedure.

Construction: Cast metal frame; sheet metal housing; plastic activator tray; rubber- and cloth-covered rubber rollers on stainless steel shafts; doors equipped with magnetic locks and cut-off microswitches.

Film-transport assembly: Capacity—100-foot rolls of 16 mm. or 35 mm. microfilm. Spindles — 2:1 ratio on 1$\frac{7}{16}$-inch radius. Flats—Front and back glass flats separable by operating "open-close" knob; can be removed for cleaning.

Maintenance: At the end of each day the bar which holds the pressure roller in place should be raised to release the pressure and the paper should be rolled back onto the supply spool. Each morning, or before printing is resumed, both the activator roller and the pressure roller should be cleaned with a damp cloth. As is shown in Figure 9, the paper drive is controlled by a switch which has three positions — "off," "run," and "jog." The rollers can be rotated for cleaning by turning the switch to "jog." When the machine is again ready for operation, the paper drive switch must be turned to the "run" position. Every two weeks the drive, pressure, and activator rollers should be removed and cleaned by washing them with warm water. Every two weeks or after every third roll, the activator tray and sponge should be removed and thoroughly washed in warm water. The sponge should then be squeezed dry and returned to the activator tray. The tray can then be replaced and refilled with fresh activator.

Fig. 9. Paper drive switch.

Cost of machine: $1,485.

Warranty: Six-month warranty covering repair or replacement of defective parts. Following the expiration of the warranty, a service contract for the maintenance of the machine is available at a minimum cost of $50.00 per year.

Operation

To use the Filmac 200-R as a reader-printer, three things are necessary: (1) a roll of Thermofax microfilm copy paper, (2) the activator which processes the exposed print, and (3) the film which is to be printed. A roll of paper stock is placed in the left-hand compartment of the machine between two hubs (Figure 10). The leading edge of the paper is drawn over the top of the machine and folded to form a "V" for easy insertion between the paper-advance rollers (Figure 11). When the leading edge has been fed through the rollers and properly aligned over the guides which support the paper along its edges, the paper-advance rollers are brought into contact by closing the clamp arm at the top of the roller assembly. The left-hand door and the cover of the machine can then be closed. A paper drive switch which has three positions — "run," "off," and "jog" — is located at the lower right-hand corner of the panel below the drive rollers. With this switch in the "jog" position, approximately three feet of paper are advanced to clear the machine of paper which had been exposed to light during the loading operation. This three-foot leader is threaded through a slot at the top of the door on the right side of the machine and torn off against the cut-off bar at the bottom edge of the slot.

Fig. 10. Paper supply assembly.

The activator tray which consists of a plastic tray and a viscous sponge is located at the upper right-hand side of the machine (Figure 12). On the outer side of the tray are two level indicator marks. The tray is filled by pouring activator from the dispensing bottle back and forth over the length of the tray until the sponge is saturated and the level of the solution has reached the upper level indicator mark. The level of the activator will go down from both use and evaporation. Since the total quantity of solution is small, the level must be checked frequently and additional activator added as needed to keep the level between the upper and lower level indicator marks.

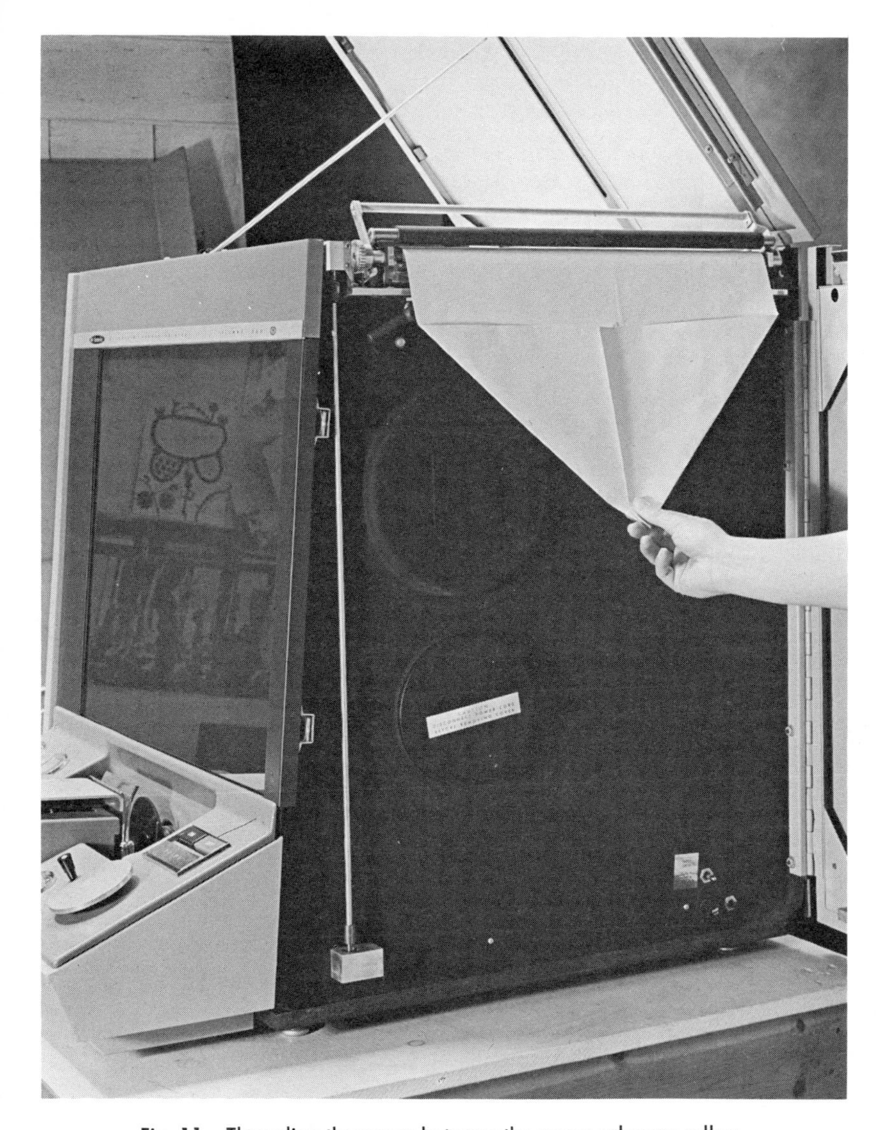

Fig. 11. Threading the paper between the paper advance rollers.

Unlike the Filmac 100, in which the coated surface of the paper passes in contact over a viscous sponge to develop the exposed image, the Filmac 200-R is equipped with a cloth cover roller which picks up activator from the sponge and applies it to the coated surface of the paper. To bring the sponge in the activator tray in contact with the cloth-covered roller, the tray is placed in position beneath the drive rollers and then elevated by means of two plastic arms — one at each end of the tray. If the machine has been out of use long enough for the cloth-covered roller to become dry, it should be rotated for a few seconds by operating the paper drive switch until it becomes wetted with activator.

The roll microfilm holder consists of two spindles on which a roll of microfilm and a take-up reel are placed, a pair of glass flats, and, on each side of the glass flats, a pair of highly polished metal rollers called "film guide assemblies" between which the film is threaded. As is shown in Figure 13, a number of controls are provided. At the right of the lamp shield is located a "film gate knob" which opens and closes the glass flats. The knob must be in

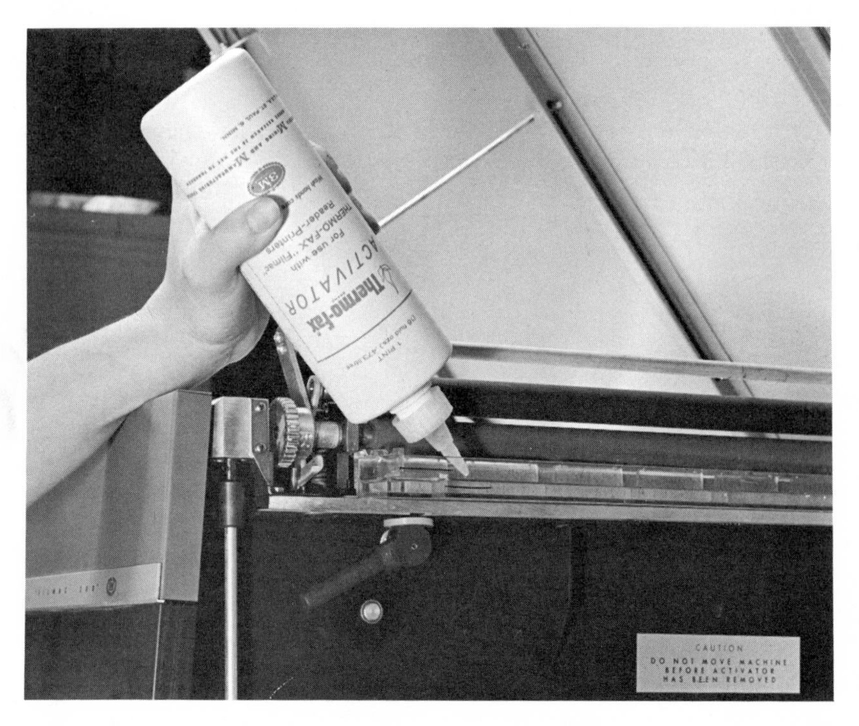

Fig. 12. Filling the activator tray.

the "open" position for threading film from the supply spool through the film guide assemblies and glass flats to the take-up reel. For viewing or printing it is turned to the "close" position. Care must be taken to make sure that the knob is turned to the "open" position before the film is advanced to a different frame. If this is not done, any dust on the surface of the film or the glass flats can cause scratches.

When the desired frame has been positioned on the screen and the glass flats closed, focusing is done by rotating the focusing ring which is located just forward of the lamp house. At the left of the lamp shield which covers the lamp house is located a "vertical card control knob." This is used for the positioning of microfilm frames mounted in EAM cards and has no function when roll microfilm is being viewed or printed. At the extreme left of the machine is located the "half and full size print selector knob." By turning it to the right a metal mask is brought into position, covering the left side of the screen image, and the paper advance is altered so that if a print is now made, only a half sheet of paper covering the area of the visible image is advanced. To the right of this knob is the "timer knob" which controls the duration of exposure. It is divided into twelve intervals marked "LT" (light), 1 through 10, and "DK" (dark). The actual duration of the exposure ranges from 2 seconds at the "light" setting to 31½ seconds at the "dark" setting.

To make a print, the timer knob is set for the desired exposure interval and the print button is pressed. At the end of the exposure

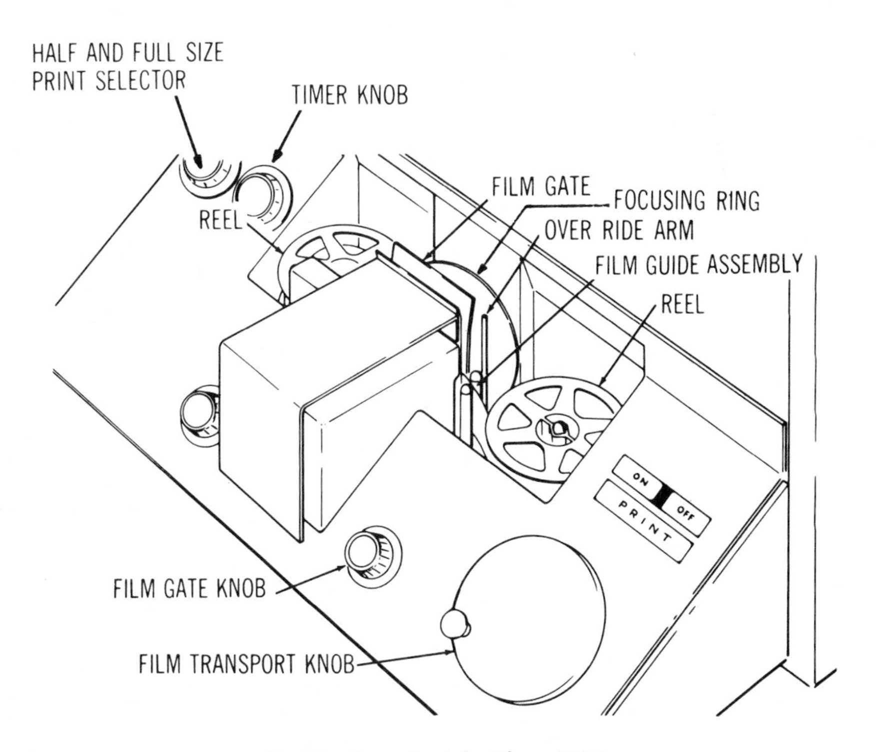

Fig. 13. Controls of the Filmac 200-R.

interval the finished print is advanced out of the machine where it can be torn off against the cut-off bar.

Analysis

The Filmac 200-R is one of the better machines tested in terms of such important features as engineering, quality of construction, ease of operation, optical performance, evenness of illumination, and ease of maintenance. Unfortunately, however, it was not designed for the production of prints from library microforms in roll form but from microfilms of engineering drawings in roll form or in EAM cards. By and large, engineering drawings mounted in EAM cards have ample borders. In the first place the drawings themselves have a border and secondly, the mounting of a frame of film in an EAM card requires a border which perforce reduces the size of the image below that which might be maximum for a 35 mm. film frame if it were not destined to be mounted in an EAM card.

The design of the machine has therefore been in keeping with what the maximum image dimensions of an engineering drawing for EAM mounting might be, whether the image was in unitized form or in roll form. This maximum image size, however, is smaller than that which is frequently encountered in microforms of various kinds of library materials. It was not, therefore, surprising to find that despite the fact that the Filmac 200-R is capable of handling 35 mm. microfilm in roll form, differences in image size between 35 mm. microfilm images of engineering drawings and, to name only one important example from a library collection — newspapers — are sufficiently different to limit seriously the utility of the machine as a reproducing device for library use.

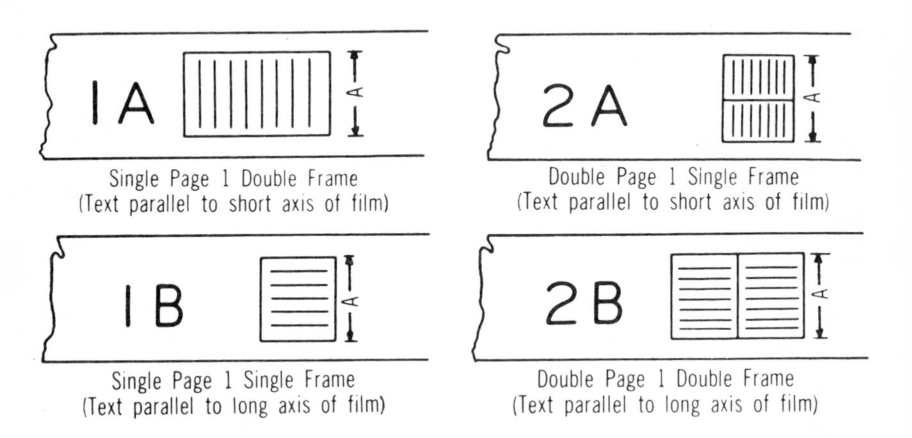

Fig. 14. Microfilm position chart.

A further design limitation is encountered with reference to the format of the two examples chosen. Engineering drawings are usually horizontal in format, the long dimension being the width of the drawing and the short dimension being the height. But newspapers often follow a reverse pattern in which the long dimension is the height and the short dimension the width. Because in the Filmac 200-R there is no provision for rotating the image, newspapers filmed in position 1-A (see Figure 14) appear on the reader screen with the lines of text reading vertically on the screen instead of horizontally (Figure 15). While this represents a considerable inconvenience in reading the screened image, prints, in most cases, can be successfully made. If, however, a newspaper has been filmed in the 2-B position, the lines of the text are then horizontal, but the image size may be too great (i.e., sufficiently larger than the image size of an engineering drawing) to permit the entire length and width of the text to be either read or printed.

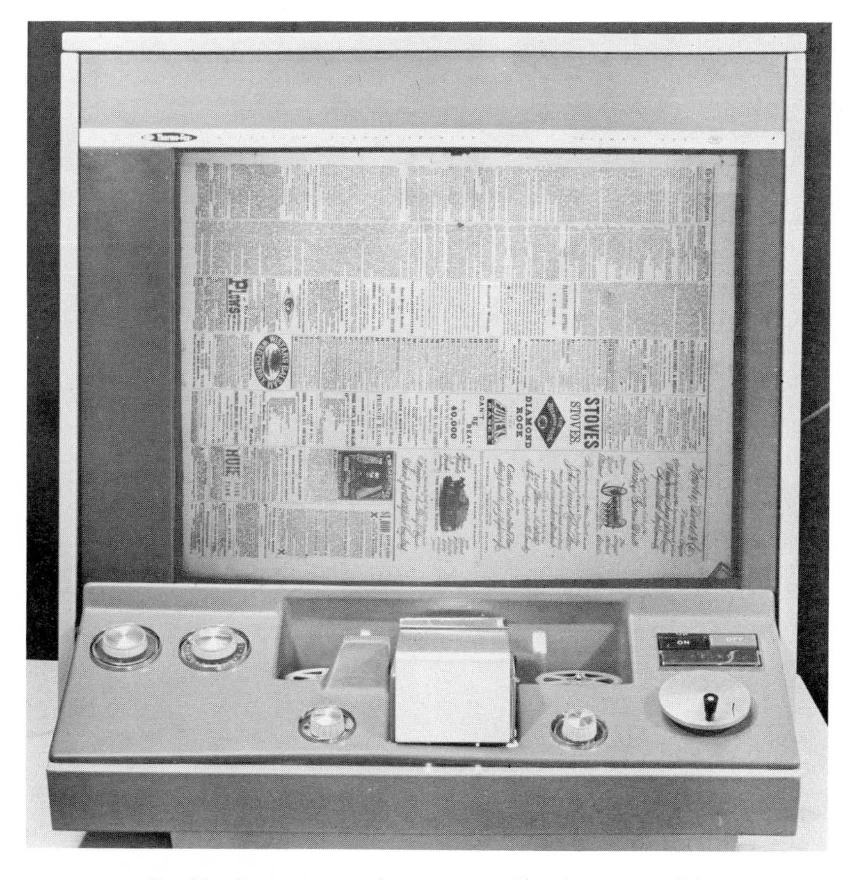

Fig. 15. Screen image of a newspaper filmed in position 1-A.

The standard non-perforated 35 mm. microfilm frame measures $1\frac{1}{4}$ by $1\frac{3}{4}$ inches. In the interests of keeping the reduction ratio used in the filming of newspapers in position 2-B as low as possible, a modification of this frame size was introduced which enlarges the image somewhat in both of its dimensions. This modified frame measures $1\frac{5}{16}$ by $1\frac{27}{32}$ inches. The extent to which the Filmac 200-R fails to print the full area of either a standard or modified frame is shown in Figures 16 and 17. How this loss affects the reproduction of two pages of a newspaper is shown in Figure 18. It is also interesting to note in this connection that the image which appears on a print is slightly smaller than that which appears on the reader screen. Approximately $\frac{1}{4}$ inch is missing at the top edge, $\frac{3}{16}$ inch from the bottom edge, and $\frac{3}{32}$ inch each from the right- and left-hand edges.

Summary

In view of the fact that one of the best known, most widespread, and commonly used of all library microforms is the newspaper file, one is tempted, at first glance, to be hopeful about a machine which produces an excellent $17\frac{1}{2}$- by 24-inch copy of a microfilm of a 35 mm. micro-image by merely pressing a button. Minor deficiencies, such as the fact that the small arms which support the activator

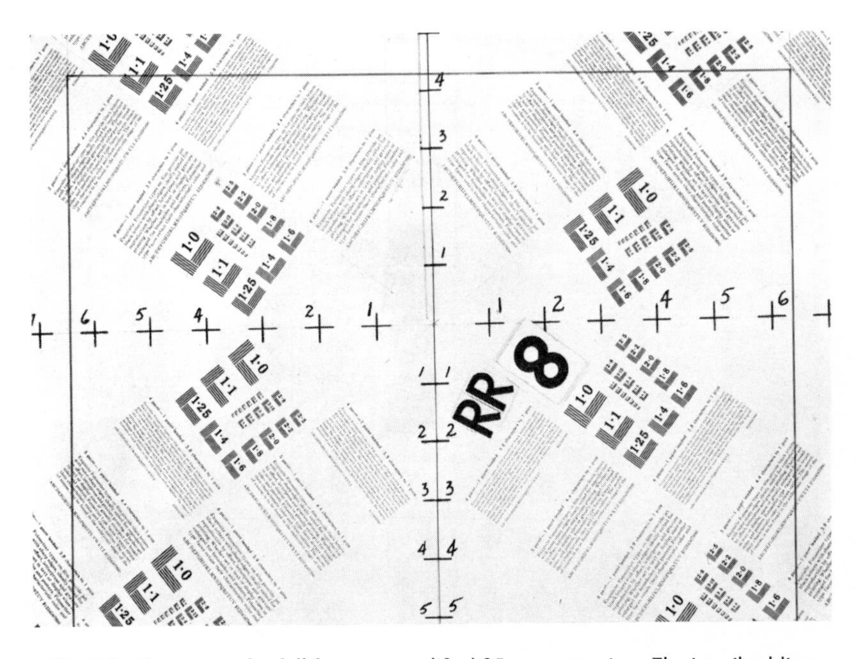

Fig. 16. Coverage of a full-frame unmodified 35 mm. negative. The inscribed lines show the maximum area that can be reproduced on a print.

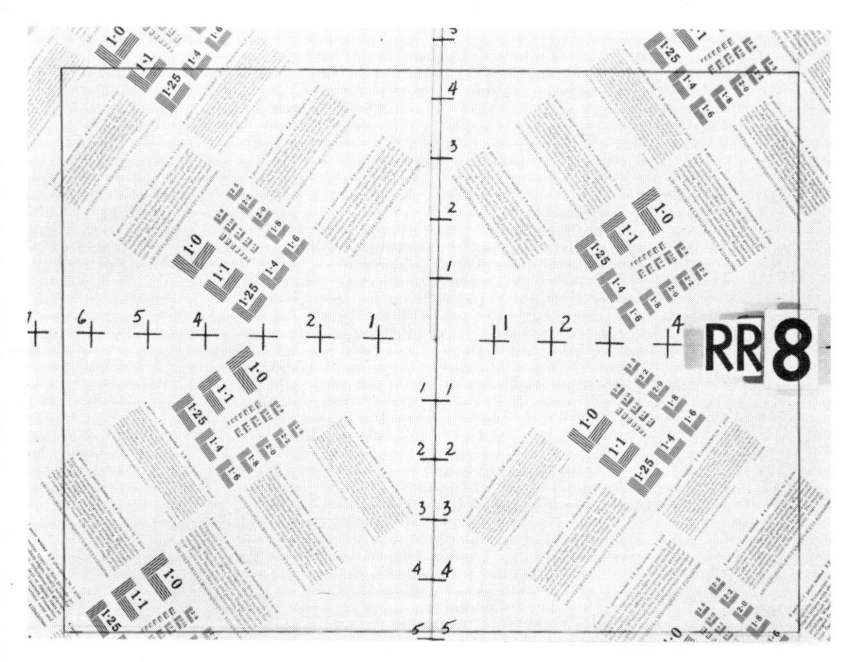

Fig. 17. Coverage of a full-frame modified 35 mm. negative. The inscribed lines show the maximum area that can be reproduced on a print.

Fig. 18. Coverage of a newspaper filmed in position 2-B. The inscribed lines show the maximum area that can be reproduced on a print.

tray in position are readily dislodged, and that they or their supporting washers can easily become lost, could be overlooked. But, the unhappy fact that newspapers filmed in the 1-A position cannot be conveniently read and newspapers filmed in the 2-B position often can neither be read nor printed negate what optical, mechanical, or automation advantages the machine might possess. For the reasons shown, it cannot be recommended for library use. By accident, this machine comes close to meeting a real library need. But because it was never designed with library microforms in mind, it does not come close enough.

6 The Filmac 300

General description

The Filmac 300 operates on the same general principles as the Models 100 and 200-R but offers far more in the way of control over image size and print size. Any desired degree of magnification within two ranges — from 7X to 11.5X and from 13X to 20X — can be obtained. Print size can be controlled from a minimum of 4 by 11 inches to a maximum of 14 by 11 inches. The machine will accept 16 mm. or 35 mm. microfilm or microfiche. Prints are produced by the electrolytic process. The data which follows is based only on demonstrations and observations since a machine has not as yet been obtained for full-scale testing.

Specifications

Manufacturer: Minnesota Mining and Manufacturing Company.

Where manufactured: United States.

Process employed: Electrolytic.

Measurements: Width—21½ inches. Depth—46 inches. Height—26 inches. Weight—220 pounds.

Size of viewing screen: 11 by 14 inches.

Size of print: Minimum—4 by 11 inches. Maximum—14 by 11 inches.

Size of image on print (maximum): 10½ by 13¼ inches.

Size of roll stock microfilm copy paper: 8½ inches by 300 feet and 11 inches by 300 feet.

Cost per roll: $25.92 (in lots of four) for 8½-inch roll. $33.53 (in lots of four) for 11-inch roll.

Lens: Aperture—f5.6. Focal lengths—80 mm. and 135 mm. Magnification range—Continuous from 7X to 11.5X and from 13X to 20X.

Focusing method: Helical mount.

Power requirements: 110/120 volts; 60 cycles; 8 amperes.

Electrical components: Paper drive motor; fan motor; mirror motor; 500-watt projection lamp; transformer; fuse.

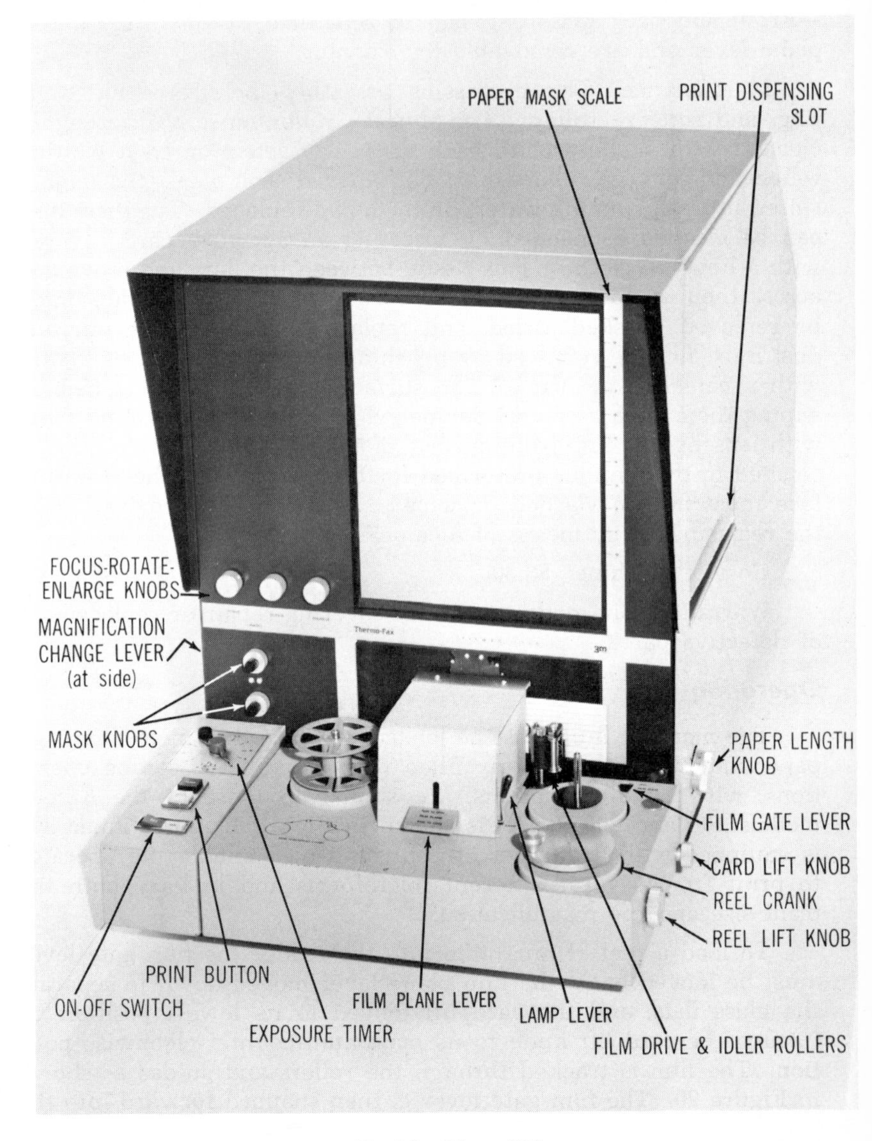

Fig. 19. Filmac 300.

To replace lamp: Remove the lamp-house cover; remove and replace lamp; replace lamp-house cover.

Construction: Cast metal and sheet metal base and housing; plastic activator tray; rubber-covered rollers on stainless steel shafts.

Film-transport assembly: Capacity—100-foot rolls of 16 mm. or 35 mm. microfilm. Spindles—2¼:1 ratio on 1½-inch radius. Flats

—Front and back glass flats can be separated by operating a film plane lever and are removable for cleaning.

Maintenance: The processing assembly includes drive, wetting, and squeeze rollers. The squeeze roller must be thoroughly cleaned with a damp cloth each day. The activator tray, wetting roller, and squeeze rollers must be removed each week, thoroughly rinsed in fresh running water, drained, and replaced. The glass flats can be cleaned as needed by inserting an aperture card covered with a lint-free cloth or lens tissue between the flats and moving it across their surfaces. For more thorough cleaning, the flats must be removed, washed, dried, and replaced. To clean the mirrors, dust must first be removed by brushing the mirror surfaces lightly with a camel's-hair brush. The surfaces may then be cleaned by wiping them with a sponge dampened in water and polishing them with lens tissue. The front surface of the projection screen may be cleaned in the manner prescribed for the mirrors but the rear surface must not be washed or wiped. Dust may be removed from the rear surface by means of a camel's-hair brush.

Cost of machine: $3,600.

Warranty: Six-month warranty covering repair or replacement of defective parts.

Operation

The machine must first be loaded with a roll of microfilm copy paper and the activator tray filled with activator. Loading operations, with minor variations, are similar to those of the Filmac models 100 and 200-R. As is shown in Figure 19, the Filmac 300 is equipped with a number of controls which enable the operator to print from several different microforms and to vary both the print size and the magnification.

To load a reel of microfilm into the reader the film gate lever must be moved back, the film plane lever moved down to separate the glass flats, and the card lift moved to its lowest position by turning the card lift knob to its maximum counter-clockwise position. The film is tracked through the rollers and guides as shown in Figure 20. The film gate lever is then snapped forward into the "close" position and the reel crank rotated until the desired image is correctly positioned horizontally on the screen. The vertical position of the image can be adjusted by turning the reel-lift knob. The film plane lever can then be closed and, if needed, the projected image can be rotated to any desired position over a range of 360 degrees by turning the rotate knob. The desired magnification is selected by moving the magnification change lever forward for lower magnification and toward the rear for higher. Final control of the image size is accomplished by turning the enlarge knob one-quarter turn in the direction desired. The image is brought into sharp focus by rotating the focus knob. Since evenness of illumination will vary at different magnifications, a lamp lever is provided which can be moved to obtain maximum screen brightness and evenness.

To control print size when making a copy, a set of four mask knobs is provided which mask off unwanted material. If a print smaller than 11 by 14 inches is needed, the film plane lever is moved down to separate the flats and the reel-lift knob turned until the lower edge of the projected image is just above the lower edge of the screen. By rotating the mask knobs, the upper mask is brought down to the top edge of the projected image and the masks at each side brought in to exclude unwanted portions of the image. The paper length knob is then set at the index number which corresponds to the height of the image as shown on the paper mask scale. The exposure timer is then set and the print button pressed to make the copy. After the copy emerges from the print-dispensing slot at the right side of the machine it can be torn off against the cut-off bar.

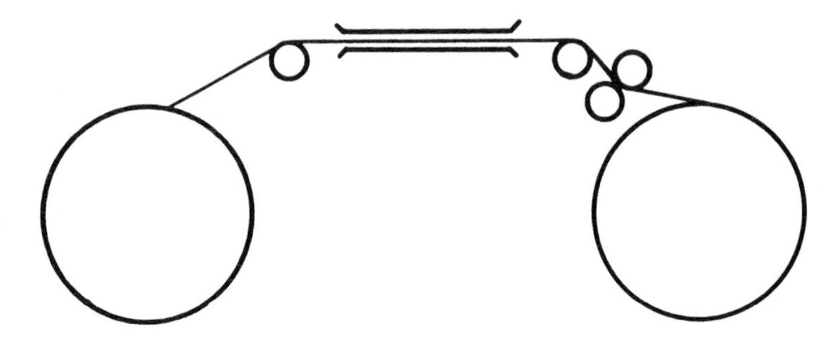

Fig. 20. Film tracking system of the Filmac 300.

Analysis

Because the data presented herein is based on the specifications supplied by the manufacturer, information gained from demonstrations, and only the most limited amount of experimentation, no full evaluation of the Filmac 300 can be attempted at this time. A number of observations can be made, however.

Like other Filmac units, the Model 300 appears to be well engineered and well constructed. The optical performance of the lens and the movable mirror system which controls magnification appear to be quite satisfactory. Although exposures must be increased for higher magnifications as the lens-to-screen distance increases, waste from incorrect exposures should still be small because of the great exposure latitude of the electrolytic process. As was brought out in the description of the operation of the machine, the advantages of extensive control over image position, magnification, and print size are gained by the provision of a much greater number of control knobs and levers than either of the other Filmac models possesses. If the machine is to be operated efficiently and economically, an operator must understand the functions of the various controls and know how and when they are to be used.

Summary

In comparison with other reader-printers, the capabilities of the Filmac 300 make it far more compatible as a device for producing enlarged copies from library microtransparencies than any of the other machines which were selected for testing. In particular, such features as a screen size of 11 by 14 inches and an almost complete control of magnifications over a range of from 7 to 20 diameters make possible the reproduction of a vastly greater percentage of the microtransparencies found in library collections than any other machine presently on the market. Unfortunately for most libraries, however, the list price of $3,600 is forbidding. As has been pointed out, the electrolytic process has both advantages and disadvantages. Also, while the machine requires more competence on the part of the operator than other Filmac units, it is still simpler and more automated in its operation than some far less versatile machines which were tested.

But, because the machine has only recently been brought out, how well it will perform over an extended period of time, or how much in the way of service, adjusting, or repairing may be required are unknowns. In terms of its design features in relation to the problems inherent in the reproduction of library microtransparencies, it has much to recommend it. In terms of its mechanical performance over an extended production period, judgment must be withheld until more data are at hand.

7 Documat Reader-Printers

General description

Documat reader-printers are internal projection reader-printers which produce a print by means of the stabilization process. In addition to being marketed by Documat, Inc., under the Documat trade name, they are also marketed by other large microfilm organizations under their own trade names. They are sold by Recordak Corporation under the name of the "Recordak Reader-Printer"; by the Photostat Corporation under the name of the "Photostat-Documat Reader-Printer"; and by Microfilm Center, Remington Rand Systems under the name of the Remington Rand "Reader-Printer Model F-468."

Apart from these name differences, which in themselves do not signify any difference in the machines, there are differences in the stabilization processing method employed. The original Documat reader-printer, which was known as the "Mark I," employed a single solution (known as a "monobath") for the developing and stabilizing of the exposed image instead of the more common two-solution method in which the print first passes through a developing and then through a stabilizing solution. Forty-five seconds were required to produce a print by this method. In the interests of speeding up the processing time the Documat "Mark II," which employs a two-solution processing method was brought out and the processing time was reduced to 25 seconds. The Recordak Corporation, however, elected to stay with the monobath system but, by using different materials, also was able to reduce the processing time to 25 seconds. The materials used in the Recordak monobath version of the Documat Mark II are manufactured by the Eastman Kodak Company. The materials used in the two-solution Mark II Documats are imported from Holland. At present there is nothing to indicate that either method has any significant advantage over the other in terms of print quality, life expectancy, or cost, but the use of a monobath does have a slight advantage in terms of convenience.

The Documat reader-printers will accept 16 and 35 mm. microfilm and microfiche and deliver prints which have an image measuring 7 by 9⅜ inches on an 8½- by 11-inch sheet of paper. Control of image size is accomplished by means of supplementary lenses which provide five degrees of magnification ranging from 10.5 diameters to 33.8 diameters.

Specifications

Manufacturer: Documat, Inc.

Where manufactured: United States.

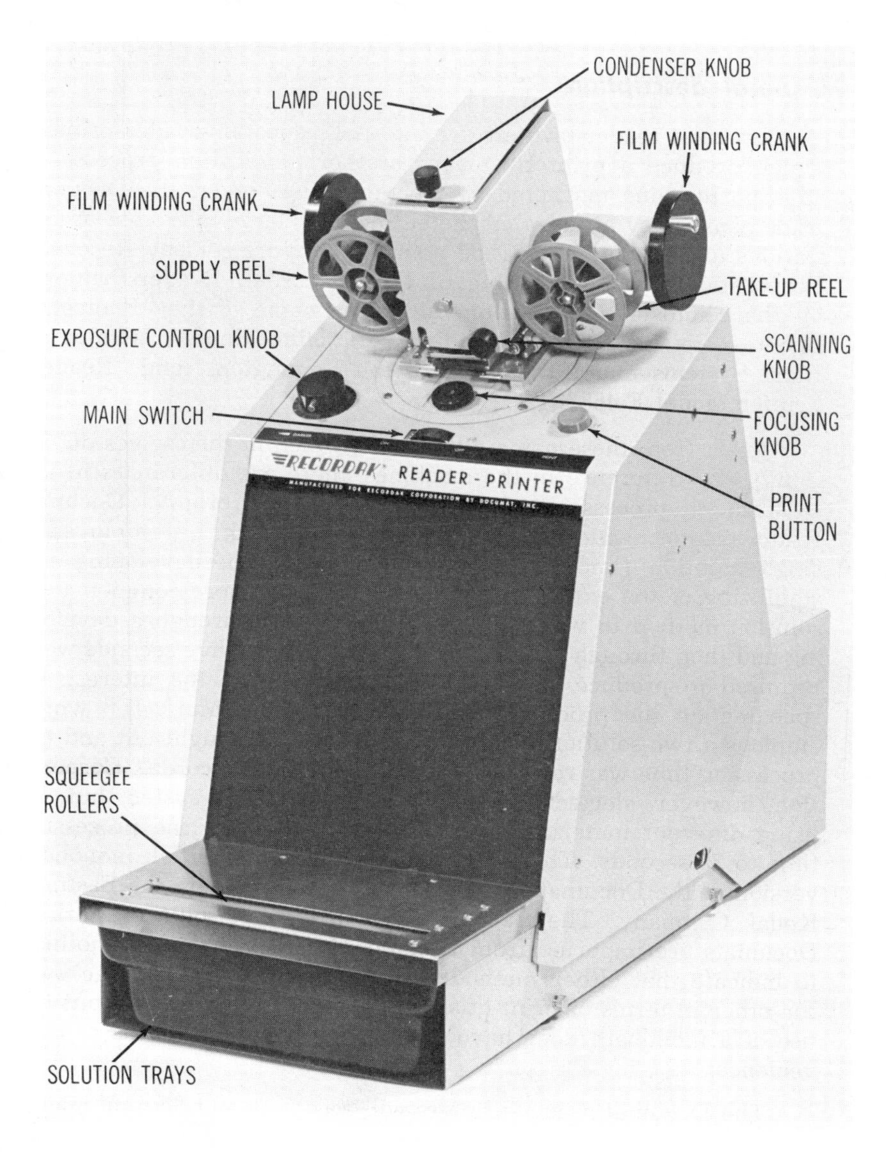

Fig. 21. The Documat Reader-Printer.

Process employed: Stabilization.

Measurements: Width—13 inches. Depth—30 inches. Height—26 inches. Weight—68 pounds.

Size of viewing screen: 11 by 11 inches.

Size of print: 8½ by 11 inches.

Size of image on print: 7 by 9⅜ inches (lines are inscribed on the 11- by 11-inch screen to indicate the area that will be reproduced on a print).

Size of roll stock sensitized paper: 8½ inches by 150 feet.

Cost per roll: $12.50 (in lots of two).

Lenses available:

Focal Length	Magnification	Recommended for Use with	Filmed at a Reduction Ratio of
52.8 mm.	10.5X	Legal-size originals	16X
42.8 mm.	13.4X	Letter-size originals	16X
30.0 mm.	20.1X	Letter-size originals	24X
22.2 mm.	27.9X	Letter-size originals	34.5X
18.5 mm.	33.8X	Letter-size originals	40X

Focusing method: Direct in-and-out movement of lens barrel controlled by knurled knob operating on a screw thread.

To changes lenses: Open access door at rear; slide lens retaining plate forward and off supporting screw to free rear end; lower rear end of lens retaining plate; remove lens and supporting spring from cylindrical lens housing; place spring on barrel of replacement lens; slide replacement lens into cylindrical lens housing; raise lens retaining plate and lock in place by sliding backward over supporting screw.

Power requirements: 117 volts; 1.6 amperes; 60 cycles.

Electrical components: Transformer; processing section drive motor; fan motor; 20-volt projection lamp.

To replace lamp: Unplug power cord from right side of reader; remove condenser adjustment knob by loosening the set screw which holds it in place. An Allen wrench for this purpose is mounted on a clip on the green crossbar inside the reader. Remove the three thumb screws which hold the lamp-house cover in place;

remove lamp and replace. Reassemble lamp-house cover and condenser adjustment knob; readjust position of condensers for maximum screen brightness and evenness.

Construction: Sheet metal housing; metal gears and chain-drive for paper advance; plastic developer and overflow trays; stainless steel guide rollers; rubber-covered, stainless steel squeegee rollers operated by nylon gears; stainless steel processing section cover.

Film-transport assembly: Capacity—100-foot rolls of 16 mm. or 35 mm. microfilm. Spindles—2:1 ratio on 1⅝-inch radius. Flats—Upper and lower glass flats held in place by spring pressure. Easily removable for cleaning. Image position—Entire film-transport assembly and illumination system can be rotated a full 360 degrees with "click" stops in each 90-degree position, and can be moved from side to side by means of a scanning device.

Paper supply: 8½-inch by 150-foot rolls sufficient to make approximately 160 prints 8½ by 11 inches in size.

Processing section: Tray capacity — Monobath models: 32 ounces. Two-solution models, (1) developer: 4½ ounces; (2) stabilizer: 22½ ounces. Solution life—Monobath models: 1 roll (150-160 prints) with water replenishment as needed to compensate for losses through evaporation and/or use, or one week. Two-solution models, one roll or two weeks, with replenishment.

Maintenance: (1) Mirrors—The fixed mirror in the Documat reader-printer which reflects the image to the screen and the movable mirror which reflects the image to the surface of the sensitized paper (Figure 22) are both of the "front surface" variety, i.e., the reflective coating is on the front surface of the glass rather than on the rear surface as is the case with ordinary mirrors. This reflective coating is very delicate and must be cleaned with great care. These mirrors should never be touched with the fingers. If dust collects on the mirrors, it can be removed by lightly brushing the surface with the camel's-hair brush supplied with the machine. Should the mirror become accidentally marred with a finger mark or smudge, it should be cleaned by wiping *very gently* with a small wad of cotton moistened with Kodak lens cleaner.

(2) Viewing screen—The front surface of the viewing screen may be cleaned with a cloth dampened in water. The rear surface, which is coated, should not be cleaned since it may become damaged in the process.

(3) Glass flats—To remove the glass flats for cleaning, the scanning knob must be rotated until the flats are brought forward as far as they will go. The upper flat is removed by lifting it and pulling it forward. The lower flat, which is held in place by the upper flat, can then be lifted and slid forward. Lens tissue or a

soft, lintless cloth may be used to clean the flats. In replacing the flats, the lower flat has rounded edges which must face upward. The upper flat has a shoulder along each edge which must be at the top. When the lower flat is in place, the shoulders of the upper

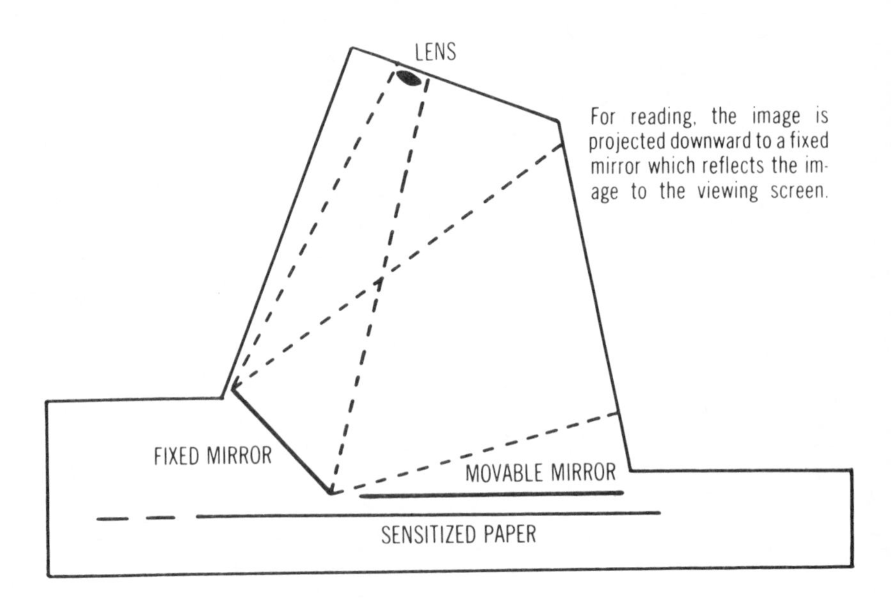

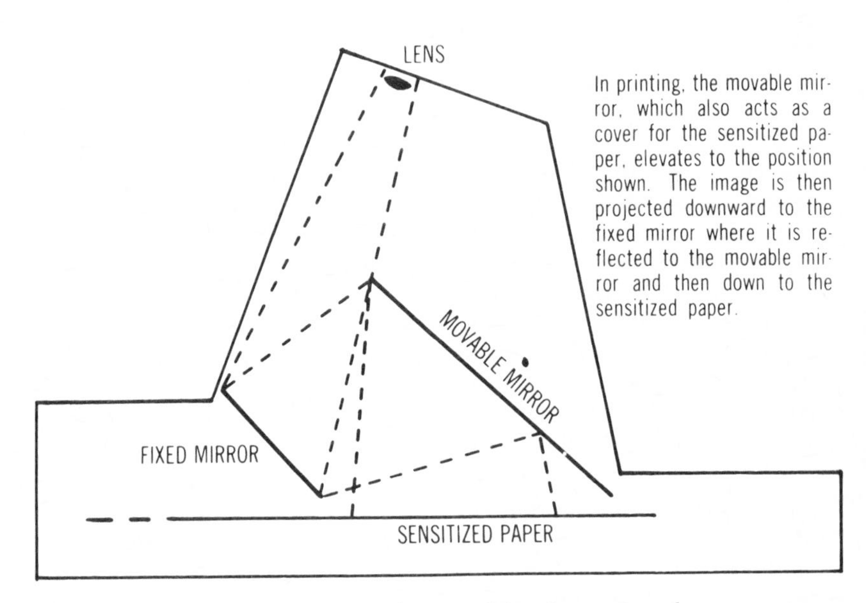

Fig. 22. Schematic diagram of the mirror system of the Documat Reader-Printer.

flat are inserted in the grooves provided and slid back until the upper flat drops into place.

(4) Lenses—If the lenses become dusty, the dust should be removed by brushing lightly with a camel's-hair brush. Should they become accidentally marred by fingerprints, they should be cleaned with lens tissue moistened with Kodak lens cleaner.

(5) Processing section—If the machine has been idle for a day or more, the squeegee rollers should be washed to remove any dried chemical deposits before any prints are made. If this is not done, brown stains may appear on the first print. After every 150 prints or after the solution has been in the machine for a week, the solution should be discarded and the solution tray, overflow tray, paper guide assembly, and squeegee rollers washed in warm water to remove any sludge or chemical deposits, dried and replaced.

(6) Lamp—When a new lamp has been installed in the machine, the condenser knob should be turned to adjust the condenser assembly group for optimum brightness and evenness of illumination.

Cost of machine: $850 with one lens.

Cost of additional lenses: $84.00 each.

Cost of rental from Recordak Corporation: $35.00 per month with one lens; additional lenses, $5.00 per month.

Warranty: One-year warranty covering repair or replacement of defective parts.

Operation (Mark 1 Model)

Before the machine can be used as a reader-printer, a roll of sensitized paper must be loaded into the rear compartment as shown in Figure 23. The leading edge of the roll of paper is inserted into the slot and guided forward to the beginning of the processing section. The roll is placed in the well provided for it. The processing tray must then be filled with the developer-stabilizer solution to the "liquid level" marker. This solution should be in a temperature range of between 65 and 80 degrees. Acceptable prints can be made at somewhat lower or higher temperatures than these but exposure and contrast then become affected. The small amount of solution absorbed in each print gradually reduces the solution level. After every 40 prints or so, *water* should be added to bring the solution level up to the "liquid level" marker.

As shown in Figure 21, a reel of film is placed on the appropriate spindle shaft so that the film leads downward off the outside of the reel and is threaded between the glass flats. The lead end of the film is then pulled through to provide enough leader to be threaded onto the take-up reel. The film can then be advanced by turning the film-winding cranks. When the desired image is in

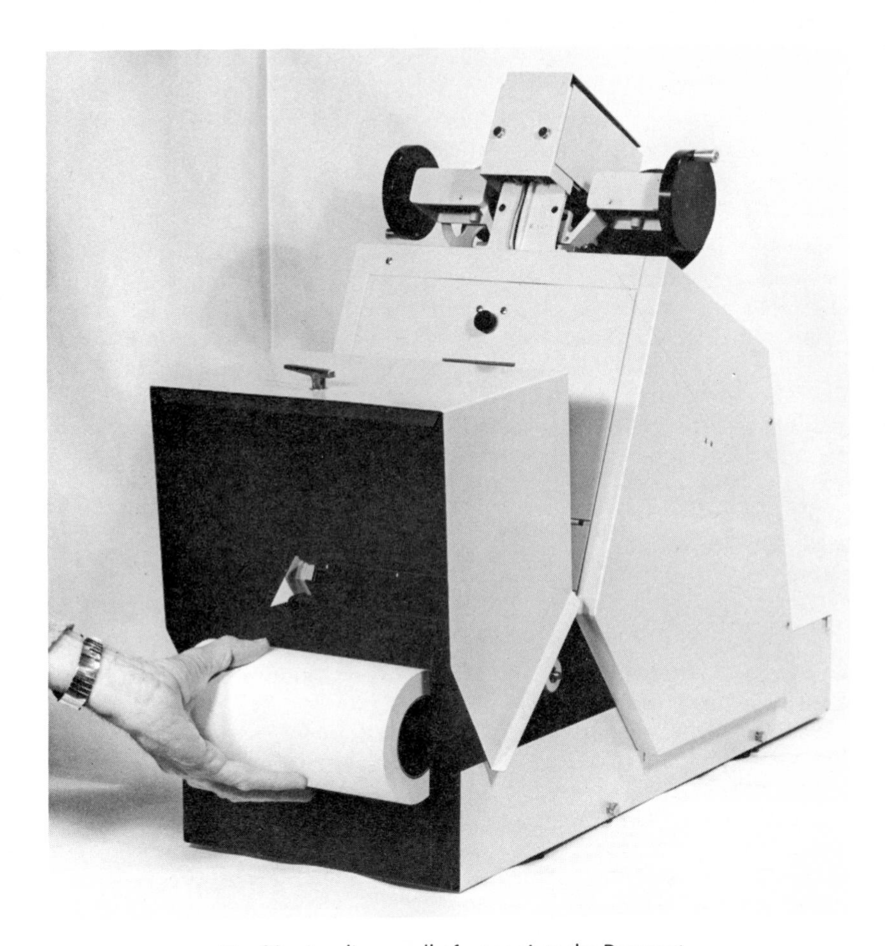

Fig. 23. Loading a roll of paper into the Documat.

place on the screen, it can be centered by turning the scanning knob. When centered, the image is brought into focus by rotating the focusing knob. The exposure control knob is marked off in a scale ranging from 0 to 100.

Unless previous experience indicates otherwise, the exposure control knob should be set at 60 for the first exposure. To make a print, all that is now required is that the print button be pressed. After an interval of 45 seconds with the Mark I model, or 25 seconds with the Mark II model, the print will emerge between the squeegee rollers at the front of the machine. If the exposure is too light, a second print will have to be made at a higher setting of the exposure control knob. A change of five units will make the next print slightly darker than its predecessor. A change of ten units will show an appreciable difference. Experience alone can show how much of a change in exposure will be required to produce a satisfactory print.

During the interval in which the sensitized paper is being exposed, the screen will be dark. As soon as the screen is again illuminated, exposure has been completed and the processing cycle has begun. At this point the operator can advance the film to the next frame for printing.

Analysis

On the whole, the Documat reader-printers are well designed and very well constructed. Certain faults, however, were noted.

The clearance between the glass flats is so small that when film is inserted between them tension from the pressure of the flats is readily noticeable. Should any dust or dirt be present on the film or in the work area where it may settle on the film, scratching of the film can readily occur. Indeed, with the Documat reader-printer tested, not only was film scratched but after a period of time the glass flats themselves showed fine scoring marks from the presence of dust on the film or the flats.

Another fault was noted in the use of the scanning device. No problems were encountered in using the 10.5 and 13.4 magnification lenses. However, with the 20.1 lens it was found that a part of one edge of a full frame could not be brought into view on the reader screen because the scanning device simply does not go far enough in one direction. The inner edge of the film being viewed can be brought into position for printing but the outer edge cannot. The loss ranges from ½ inch of original size on materials recorded at an 8 to 1 reduction ratio to approximately 1¾ inches at a 20 to 1 reduction ratio. If, for example, one wished to make a print of an article from a newspaper filmed at a 20 to 1 reduction ratio, it might be impossible to position a portion of the article within the printing area of the screen.

The focusing mechanism, although adequate, left something to be desired in terms of ease of use, the fault lying primarily in the fact that the movement of the lens in relation to the movement of the knob is too small. The knob must be turned many times before appreciable changes in focus are evident. This makes the process of bringing an image into sharp focus a slow one.

Also, as the focusing knob is turned to decrease the lens-to-film distance the movement of the lens and the corresponding change in the focus of the image is smooth, but as the knob is turned in the other direction, which increases the lens-to-film distance, the movement is jerky. The knob may be rotated once or twice without any apparent change in the appearance of the image, but with the next turn a great change in focus suddenly occurs as the lens drops to a lower position. This, too, tends to make focusing slow and somewhat tedious. A helical focusing system would be preferable.

Changing lenses must be done with considerable care because, if a lens were dropped in removing it, it could easily fall against the fixed mirror which reflects the image to the screen and permanently damage it.

Relatively speaking, the faults in the Documat reader-printer which were noted are minor in comparison with those of several other reader-printers tested. But in terms of its utility as a reader-printer for reproducing library microforms it leaves a great deal to be desired, simply because the machine was never designed to reproduce the diverse sizes and types of documents which make up library collections of microforms. As the table of lenses given in the specifications shows, the screen size, print size, and image area were established with the idea in mind of reproducing the office records of business, industry, and government which ordinarily measure 8½ by 11 inches, and the magnifications of the lenses in relation to the image size were selected to correlate with the film formats and reduction ratios most commonly used in the filming of such records. Library materials, however, are by no means so uniform in size, and the microforms made of them cannot thereby be as conveniently standardized in reduction ratio or format.

A common format employed in microfilming library materials is the full frame of 35 mm. non-perforated film, which measures 1¼ by 1¾ inches. Maps, graphs, folding plates, manuscript materials, newspapers, and various other types of originals are frequently filmed on this full frame. With the 10.5X and 13.4X lenses, full-frame negatives can be reproduced on the Documat, but only in sections. With the 10.5X lens, four prints will be required. With the 13.4X lens, eight prints will be required. With the 20.1 lens the limitation of the scanning device prevents the reproduction of the entire area of a full frame but were the margins such that the text could be brought into view, a total of 15 prints would be required to reproduce the entire frame. Not only does such sectional printing make the cost of prints excessively high but the result is then a jigsaw puzzle of many pieces which is highly unsatisfactory as a record to read from.

Table 4 shows in the left-hand columns the dimensions of the area which can be filmed on a full frame of 35 mm. non-perforated film at reduction ratios ranging from 7 to 20.1. The right-hand columns show how little of this area can be reproduced on a single print made with either the 10.5X, the 13.4X, or the 20.1X lenses. Expressed in percentages, the 10.5X lens reproduces 27.2 percent of the area of a full frame, the 13.4X lens reproduces 16.7 percent, and the 20.1X lens only 7.43 percent.

Table 5 shows the reduction ratio which must be employed in

the filming of four typical serials if the entire text area of a single page is to be reproduced on a single print when using the 10.5X, 13.4X, and 20.1X lenses.

TABLE 4

Reduction Ratio	Dimensions in Inches of Area Microfilmed on Full 1¼- by 1¾-Inch Frame, Non-Perforated 35 mm. Film (Recordak MRD-2 Camera)	Dimensions in Inches of Area which can be Reproduced on a Single 7- by 9⅜-inch Print.		
		10.5X Lens	13.4X Lens	20.1X Lens
7	8.75 x 12.25	4.66 x 6.25	3.66 x 4.9	2.43 x 3.26
8	10.00 x 14.00	5.33 x 7.14	4.18 x 5.6	2.78 x 3.73
9	11.25 x 15.75	6.0 x 8.04	4.7 x 6.3	3.12 x 4.2
10	12.5 x 17.5	6.66 x 8.93	5.22 x 7.0	3.48 x 4.66
10.5	13.125x 18.375	7.0 x 9.375	....	....
11	13.75 x 19.25	7.33 x 9.82	5.75 x 7.7	3.83 x 5.13
12	15.0 x 21.00	8.0 x 10.71	6.27 x 8.4	4.18 x 5.6
13	16.25 x 22.75	8.66 x 11.61	6.79 x 9.1	4.53 x 6.06
13.4	16.75 x 23.45	....	7.0 x 9.375	....
14	17.5 x 24.5	9.33 x 12.5	7.31 x 9.8	4.88 x 6.53
15	18.75 x 26.25	10.0 x 13.39	7.84 x 10.5	5.22 x 7.0
16	20.0 x 28.0	10.66 x 14.29	8.36 x 11.2	5.57 x 7.46
17	21.25 x 29.75	11.33 x 15.18	8.88 x 11.9	5.92 x 7.93
18	22.5 x 31.5	12.0 x 16.07	9.4 x 12.6	6.27 x 8.40
19	23.75 x 33.25	12.66 x 16.96	9.93 x 13.3	6.62 x 8.86
20	25.0 x 35.0	13.33 x 17.86	10.45 x 14.0	6.97 x 9.33
20.1	25.125x 35.175	....	....	7.0 x 9.375

TABLE 5

Subject	Text Dimensions in Inches (Single Page)	Reduction Ratio Required in Filming to Permit Reproduction of One Page on One Print		
		10.5X Lens	13.4X Lens	20.1X Lens
Unesco Bulletin for Libraries	4⅝ x 7⅞	9	11.5	17
College and Research Libraries	5³⁄₁₆ x 8	9	11.5	17
Photo Science and Technique	6⅞ x 9⅜	11	14	20
American Documentation	6¾ x 9¼	11	14	20

Since journals of the sizes shown can be, and frequently are, filmed at a reduction ratio of ten times, it will be seen from this table that if the 10.5X lens is used, only the two smaller journals can be reproduced with the full text of a single page on a single print. The larger journals would require two prints for each single page. If the 13.4X lens is used, no page could be reproduced in a single print. In each case two prints would be required. If the 20.1X lens were used, three prints would be required for the *Unesco Bulletin for Libraries,* and four prints for each of the three larger journals.

Summary

The desirable features exhibited by the Documat reader-printer — the fact that it is on the whole quite a well-designed and well-constructed machine; that it is an internal projection reader-printer which can be operated under conditions of normal room illumination; that it is capable of delivering a sharp, clear, black-and-white print in only 25 seconds — these distinct advantages are more than outweighed by the limitations imposed by the relatively small image size and the limited number of fixed magnifications. The machine was never designed for reproducing library microforms but for the reproduction of office records. When used for the reproduction of the microforms for which it was designed, it functions quite satisfactorily, and insofar as certain types of library microforms may happen to coincide in their reduction ratio and format with office record microforms, it will function satisfactorily. Unfortunately, however, too many library microforms will not fit the limitations of the machine and in such cases the Documat reader-printer will not be capable of the kind of efficient and economical performance that will fit the needs and the pockets of the librarian or scholar.

8 The Rollacopy and the Micromate

General description

"Rollacopy" and "Micromate" are trade names which have been given to a piece of equipment, or rather an assemblage of equipment which, except for the timing device and processing unit, is manufactured by the Federal Manufacturing and Engineering Corporation in Garden City, New York. "Rollacopy" is the trade name used for this equipment by one supplier — Andrews Paper and Chemical Company — and "Micromate" by at least two others — Photorapid Corporation of America and Burton Mount Corporation. The unit tested was supplied by Andrews Paper and Chemical Company and hence its trade name will be used to refer to this equipment.

The Rollacopy consists of a metal baseboard and a vertical column on which a Model 705 Federal microfilm projector is mounted. To this has been added an easel consisting of a base and a hinged glass cover for holding the sensitized paper flat, an F-R brand exposure timing device, and a Polymicro two-bath stabilization processing unit imported from France. The size of the image is controlled by raising or lowering the projector head on the column. The projector accommodates 16 mm. or 35 mm. microfilm and is equipped with spindles for standard 100-foot reels.

Specifications

Manufacturers: Federal Manufacturing and Engineering Corporation; Polyclair.

Where manufactured: United States and France.

Process employed: Stabilization.

Measurements: Width—27½ inches. Depth—25 inches. Height—37 inches. Weight—38 pounds.

Over-all size of easel: 11 by 15¼ inches.

Printing surface: 8½ by 14 inches.

Lens: Make—Schneider Componar. Aperture—Maximum: f4; minimum: f32 (click-stop iris diaphragm). Magnification—Continuous from 4X to 12X. Image sizes—Minimum: (4X) 5 by 6¾ inches; maximum (12X) 16 by 22 inches. Focal length—60 mm.

Focusing method: Helical mount.

Power requirements: 120 volts; 550 watts; 60 cycles.

Electrical components: Cooling fan; exposure timer; processing unit drive motor; 300-watt G.E. CWD projection lamp.

To replace lamp: Remove screws on both sides of lamp-house cover and remove cover. Remove louvered metal lamp shield by pulling forward. Remove lamp, replace, and reassemble.

Construction: Base—Metal plate. Column—Metal with chrome finish. Projector—Metal housing; lens mount; spindles. Timer—

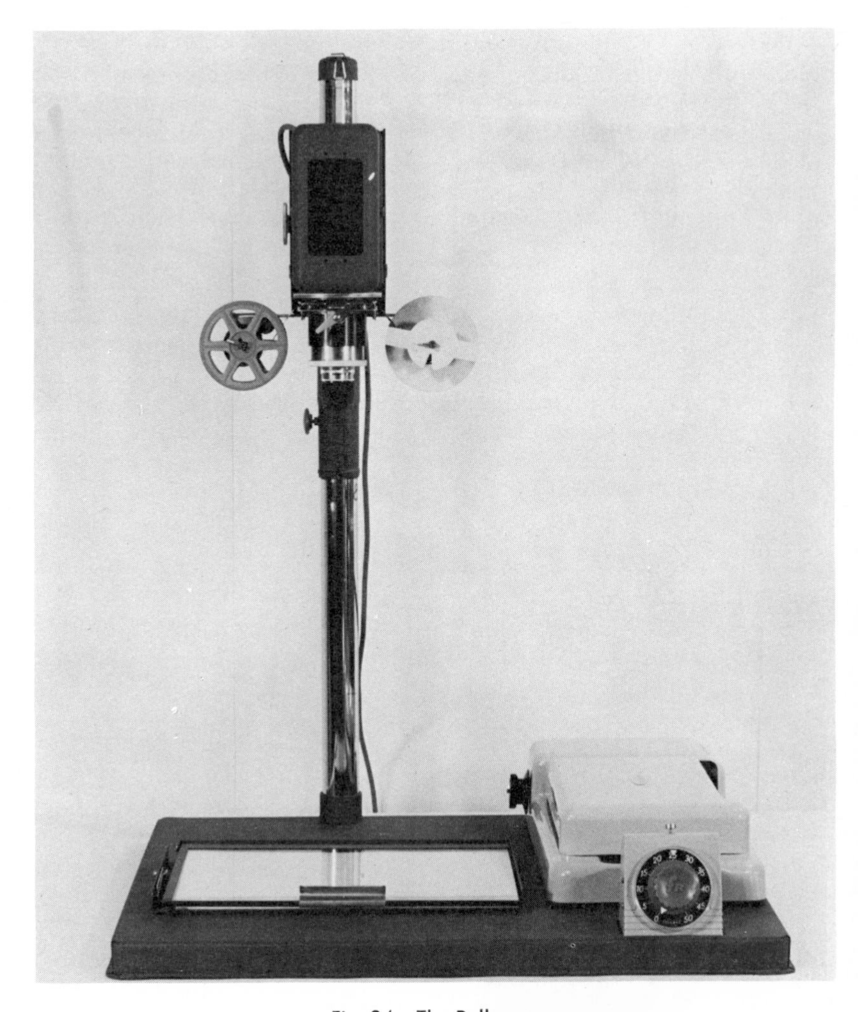

Fig. 24. The Rollacopy.

Plastic housing. Easel—Metal frame with sponge-rubber bed covered with white plastic; glass cover mounted in hinged metal frame equipped with support arm. Processing unit—Plastic housing and cover; rubber-covered rollers on stainless steel shafts; plastic gears.

Film-transport assembly: Capacity—100-foot rolls of 16 mm. or 35 mm. microfilm. Spindles—1:1 ratio on 1½-inch turning radius. Flats—upper and lower glass flats mounted in a removable, hinged metal frame equipped with a cam lever for separating the flats when film is being advanced.

Processor: Model—Polymicro Model 1. Type—2-bath stabilization process. Manufacturer—Polyclair. Where manufactured—Paris, France. Price if purchased separately—$175. Tray capacity—Developer: 8 ounces; stabilizer: 13 ounces. Width—9 inches. Maximum size print accommodated—8½ by 14 inches (see "Analysis"). Drive—Plastic gears. (The Polymicro can also be obtained with pulley and belt drive.) Recommended solution life—1 week or 300 prints. (Two larger models are available—the Model II [11 inches wide] and the Model III [17 inches wide]. These are priced at $195 and $215, respectively.)

Maintenance: Glass flats, lens, and easel should be kept clean. When chemicals are changed, trays and rollers should be cleaned in lukewarm water, drained, and reassembled. (See "Analysis.")

Cost of machine: $395.

Warranty: Unstated.

Operation

The Polymicro processing unit supplied with the Rollacopy contains two wells — one for the developing solution and one for the stabilizing solution. These trays should be filled with their respective solutions to the top of the plastic level indicators. Both solutions should be within a temperature range of from 65 to 80 degrees.

As shown in Figure 25, a reel of film is placed on the left-hand spindle of the projector and threaded between the upper and lower glass flats of the hinged film carrier (Figure 26) to a take-up spool on the right-hand spindle. In threading film through the flats or when advancing the film from frame to frame, the cam lever at the front of the film carrier is moved to a vertical position to separate the glass flats and prevent scratching of the film. When the desired frame has been located, this cam lever is moved to the position shown in Figure 27, thus permitting the flats to close. The projection lamp is turned on by pressing the button at the top of the exposure timer. The size of the projected image can then be adjusted by raising or lowering the projector on the column and

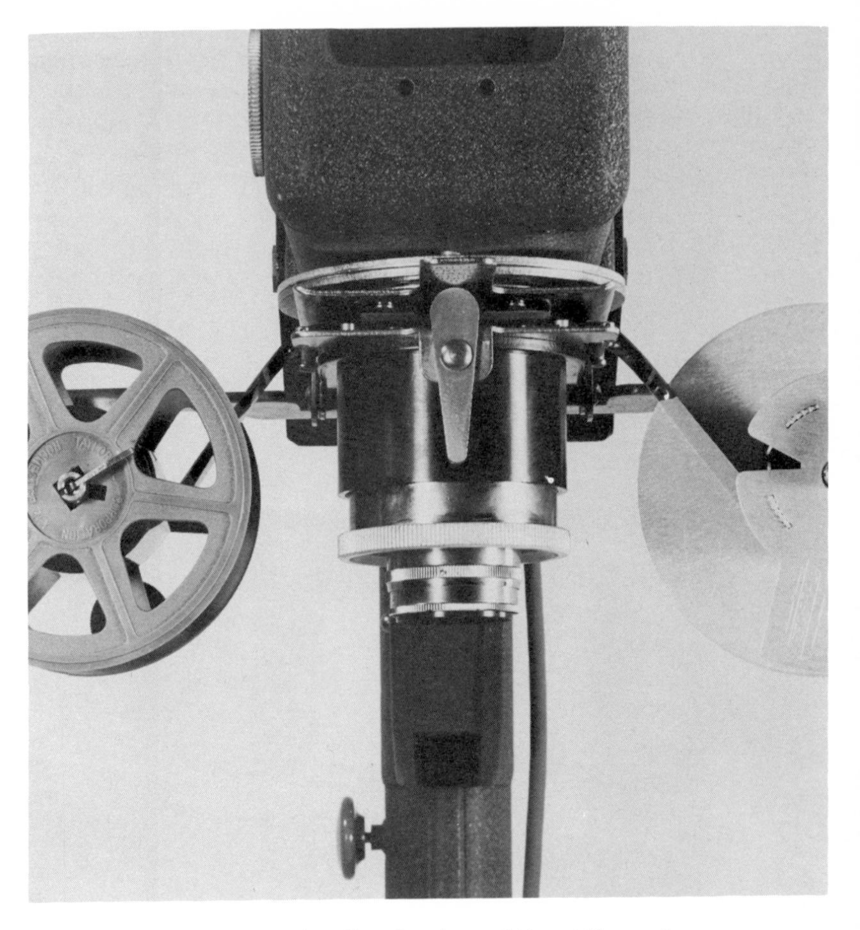

Fig. 25. Loading film. Cam lever of hinged film carrier in "open" position to separate glass flats.

the image focused by rotating the large knurled ring immediately above the lens.

Focusing should be done with the iris diaphragm of the lens at its largest opening. If greater sharpness is needed at the corners of the projected image, or if it is necessary to reduce the amount of light, this iris diaphragm can be closed to a smaller aperture. The apertures (also known as "stops") range from f4, which is the largest, through f32, which is the smallest, the intermediate stops being marked f5.6, f8, f11, f16, and f22. For each successive decrease in the size of the aperture, the exposure required to make a print will be doubled. For example, if a 10-second exposure is required at f8, a 20-second exposure will be required if the lens aperture is changed to f11.

When the image has been brought into sharp focus, the exposure interval can be set by pulling out the plastic "setting ring" which surrounds the exposure interval dial and rotating it until the triangular pointer is opposite the desired setting. The projection lamp can then be turned off by rotating the large, knurled control knob to the left until it stops at the preselected setting. With

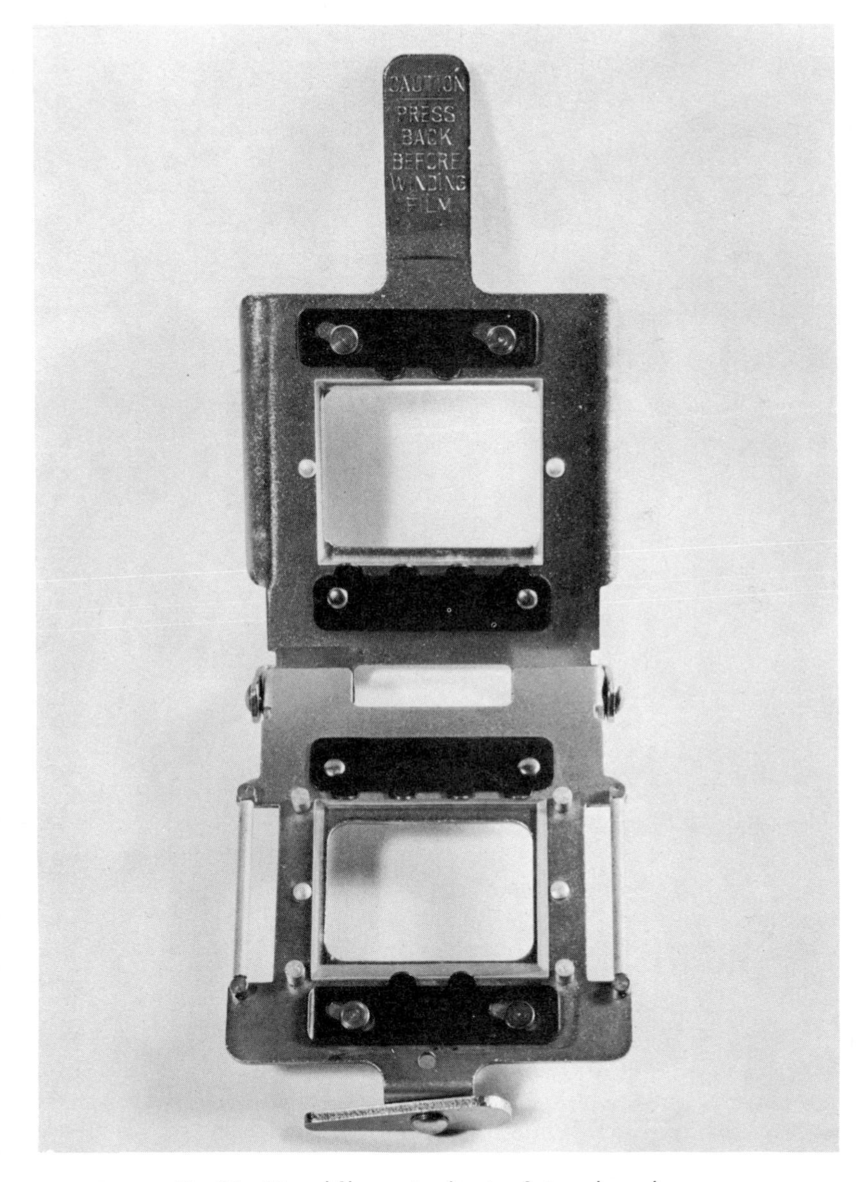

Fig. 26. Hinged film carrier showing flats and cam lever.

the projection lamp off and the timer set, a sheet of sensitized paper is then placed face *up* on the easel under the glass cover plate (Figure 28) and the exposure made by pressing the button at the top of the exposure timer. When the projection lamp goes off, the paper is then removed from the easel and fed into the processor face *down* (Figure 29). When the sheet emerges from the processor

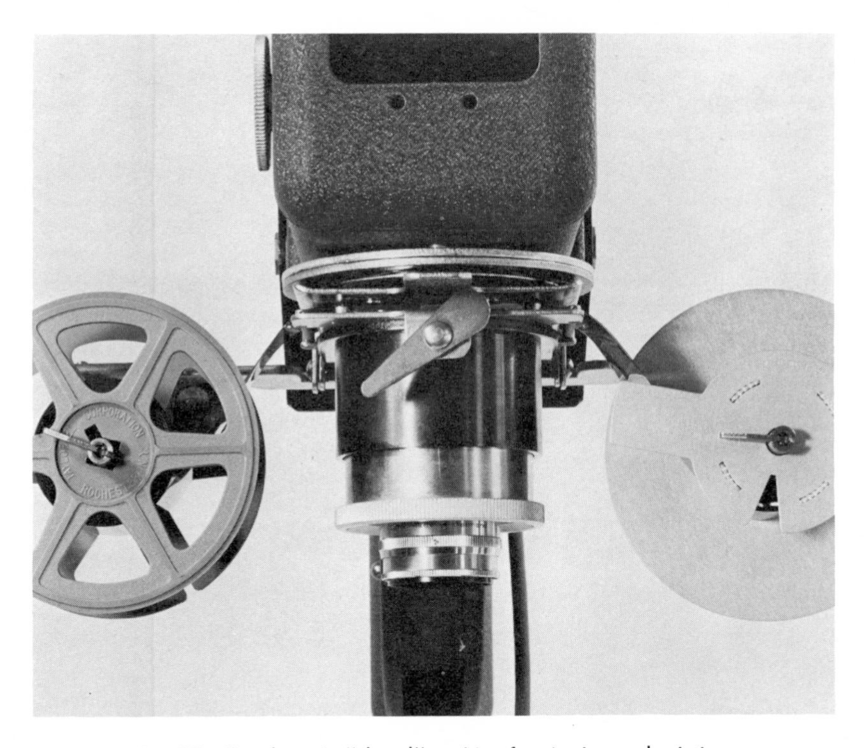

Fig. 27. Cam lever in "closed" position for viewing and printing.

it can then be examined to determine whether the exposure was satisfactory. If the print is too light, either a larger lens aperture and/or a longer exposure interval will be required. If the print is too dark, a smaller lens aperture and/or a shorter exposure interval will be required. If the print shows an over-all grayishness which interferes with legibility (assuming that the paper has not received any previous exposure to light) the print has received too much exposure to ambient light. This can be eliminated in three ways:

(a) By using a larger lens aperture (and maximum care in shielding the emulsion surface of the paper from light as much as possible) so that the length of time the sensitized surface is exposed to ambient light is much shorter.

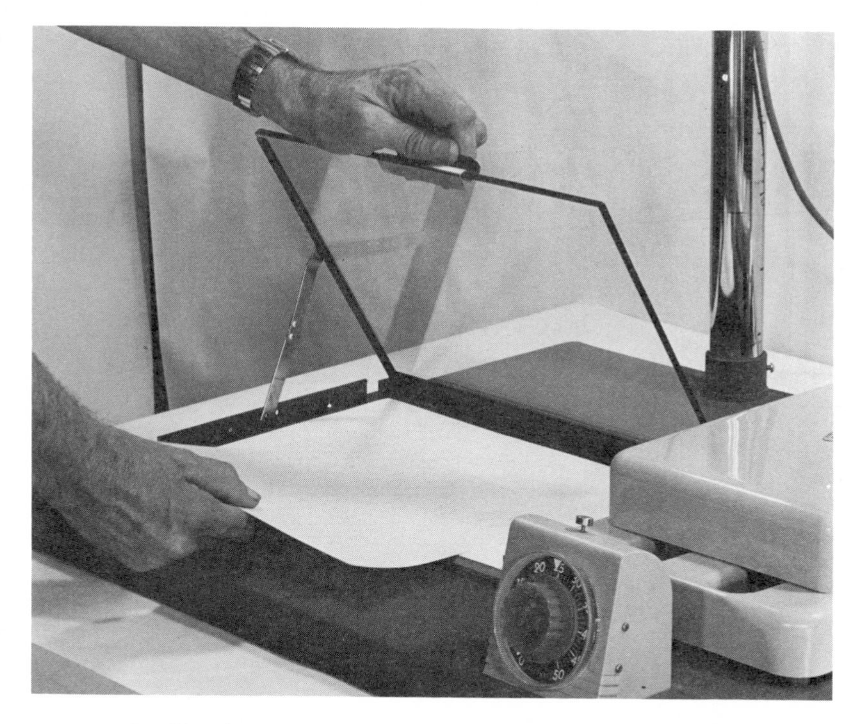

Fig. 28. Placing a sheet of sensitized paper under the easel glass.

(b) By reducing the amount of ambient light in the work area.

(c) By using a slower paper which will not be so readily affected by ambient light.

Analysis

Projection components. A number of minor construction faults were noted, none of which seriously impaired the quality of the prints produced, but which interfere with ease and convenience of use.

The cam surface of the lever which holds the glass flats apart when film is being advanced is rounded and can easily become dislodged from the "open" position when the spindle cranks are being turned, thus creating the hazard of scratching the film.

The projector employed was originally designed for use in a horizontal position. In this position the spindle cranks are underneath the film reels. When the projector is mounted on a vertical column the spindle cranks are at the rear of the film reels which makes winding the film somewhat awkward. Also, the smallness of the turning radius of the spindles makes winding through a full reel of film a somewhat tedious operation.

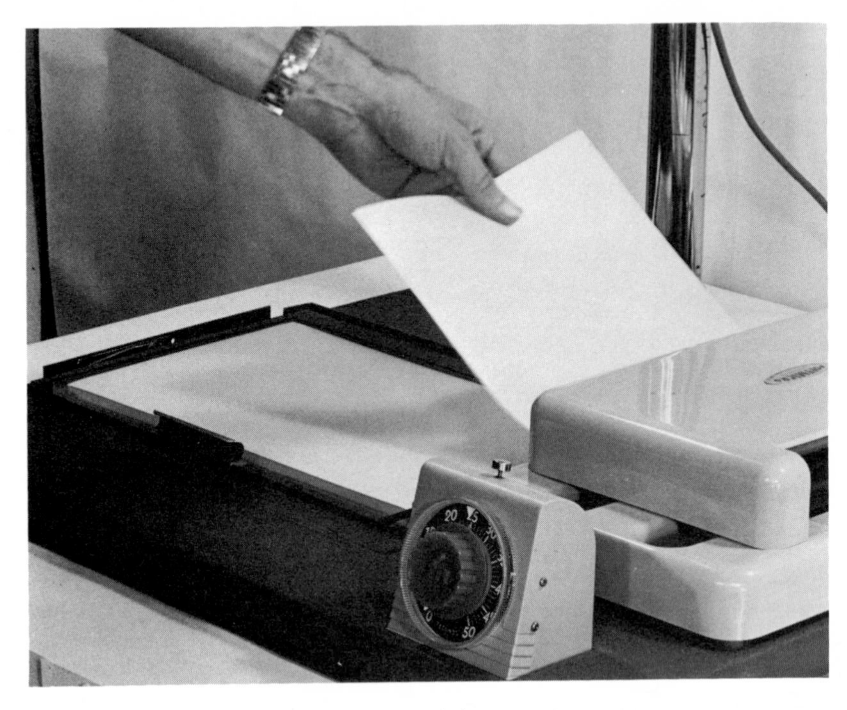

Fig. 29. Feeding an exposed sheet into the processor.

The lamp-house cover is held in place with two screws which pass through holes in the cover and screw into the base of the projector. The holes in the cover are not accurately stamped and thus do not quite match the screw holes. This makes removal and replacement of the screws somewhat difficult.

The mask beneath the lower glass flat in the film carrier has rounded corners instead of square ones. These rounded corners cut off part of the image of a full-frame 35-mm. negative. If they were square, the full frame could be projected. In practical terms this might seldom cause any problems because most microfilm images have some border, but the rounded corners make the positioning of a full frame unnecessarily difficult.

The focusing mechanism consists of two metal cylinders, one enclosing the other. The inner one, in which the lens is mounted, is equipped with three ball bearings on its outer surface which are held in place by spring pressure. These bearings travel on a helical track which is cut into the inner surface of the outer cylinder. The machining of these components is such that the helical movement is not smooth and true. As the inner cylinder is rotated there is some lateral shifting of the image which is jerky and disturbing and makes precise focusing difficult. In addition, the column on which the unit is mounted is not rigid enough to support the weight of the projector without movement when focusing is being done. The higher the projector is on the column, the more shaky the whole assembly becomes.

The plastic knob which is used to lock the projector at any given elevation on the column is too small for convenient use. Because of its small size it is difficult to tighten it sufficiently to prevent side-to-side movement of the projector when the spindle handles are turned.

Processing section. The Polymicro Model I processing unit consists of two assemblies and a cover (Figure 30). The first assembly consists of a base on which the roller drive motor is mounted and a plastic cover which contains two shallow wells for the developer and stabilizer solutions and an air vent for the motor. The second assembly consists of a series of rubber-covered rollers on stainless steel shafts which rotate at the same speed by means of a series of plastic gears. One of the stabilizer rollers is used as the main drive roller for the assembly and is mounted on a shaft which is keyed to fit the motor shaft. This roller assembly fits over the solution wells and is held firmly in place by means of four stainless steel pins. The wells are slightly longer than the roller assembly and are equipped with plastic indicator markers for control of the solution level. With the rollers in place (Figure 31), a plastic cover is then placed over the roller assembly to protect the sensitized material from unnecessary exposure to light and to minimize evaporation of the solutions (Figure 32).

Two design weaknesses were noted. The opening into which

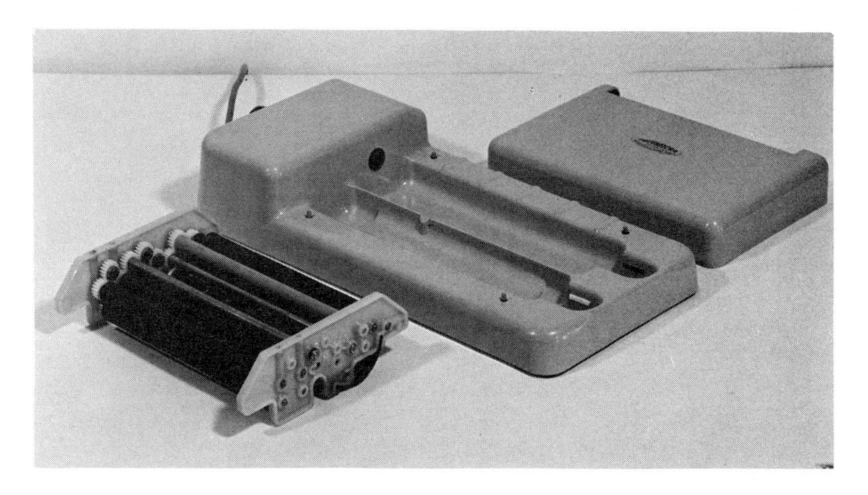

Fig. 30. Base (containing motor and solution wells), roller assembly, and cover of Polymicro processing unit.

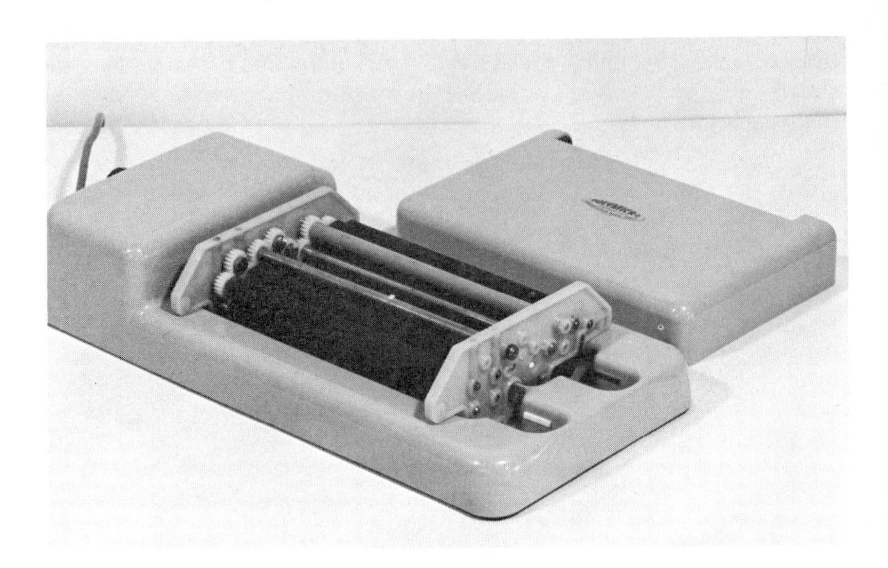

Fig. 31. Roller assembly in position.

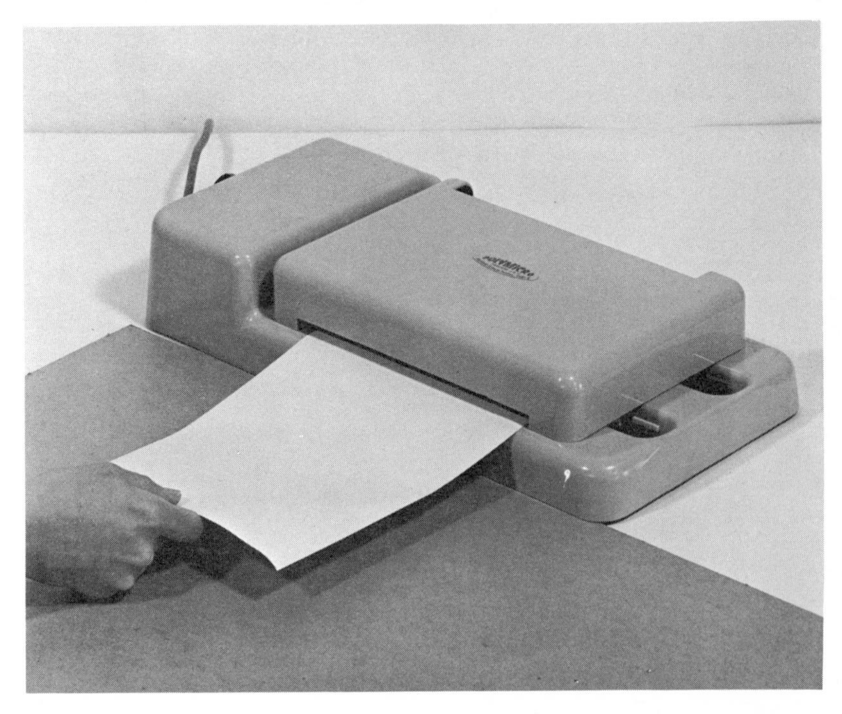

Fig. 32. Cover in place. Sheet being fed into processor. Note the narrow clearance between the edges of the feeding slot in the cover and the edges of the 8½-inch-wide sheet.

the exposed sheet of paper is passed is only 9 inches wide (Figures 32 and 33). This means that care must be taken in feeding sheets 8½ inches wide into the processor since there is only ¼ inch of leeway on each side of the sheet. If the least skewing of the paper occurs in feeding it in, the leading edge may catch on the cover when the sheet emerges or the trailing edge may become damaged by being forced against the flanges that support the roller shafts on one end or the gear teeth on the other. It was found that straight feeding was a little easier to do if the cover was removed so that the operator could see the position of the leading edge of the paper against the developer rollers; but ambient light conditions had to be such that this additional period of exposure to light did not result in fog.

Fig. 33. Removing processed sheet as it emerges from the processor.

The second weakness lies in the fact that the solutions are not in separate trays removable for easy cleaning but are in wells in the assembly which contains the drive motor. This means that for thorough cleaning of residual chemicals from the trays, the entire assembly, including motor and power cord, must be taken to a sink. Because, of course, it is absolutely necessary to prevent any of the electrical components from becoming wet, cleaning must be done with great care. Other stabilization processing units such as the Fotorite and the processing section of the Universel are much easier to clean because the solutions are in removable trays which can be taken to a sink and freely scrubbed and washed with running water.

Materials. The Andrews Paper and Chemical Company supplies a line of papers for use with the Rollacopy which are manufactured in France by Ets. Bauchet et Cie. These papers are currently available in either a transparent or an opaque base and may be obtained in two speeds — grade "Q5" which is very slow, and can be used for contact printing, and grade "M5" which is quite fast and can be used for printing with the Rollacopy. A paper having an intermediate speed, which was designated as grade "L5," has been discontinued.

Rollacopy Q5 (slow) paper, which can be handled under conditions of ordinary room illumination, was found to be much too slow to be practical with the Rollacopy. From a negative having a background density of 1.20 at a magnification of 10 diameters, an exposure at 115 volts of 60 seconds at the largest lens opening (f4) was required to produce an image strong enough to be easily read. Definition, however, was not satisfactory at the edges of the print. A fully satisfactory print of the test negative which would be sharp to the edges would require a lens aperture of at least f11 and an exposure of eight minutes.

Prints made from the same negative on Rollacopy M5 (fast) paper required exposures ranging from ¾ second at the largest lens opening to 13 seconds at an aperture of f16. The print made at f16 was sharp to the edges, but since the M5 paper is more than 60 times as fast as Q5 paper, the printing operations must be conducted under virtually darkroom conditions. On average subjects, voltage variations of plus or minus 5 volts had little effect on legibility, but on finely detailed subjects variations in excess of 5 volts may cause breaking or filling of fine lines and spaces in letters or numerals.

The field of illumination is markedly uneven. A test negative which had resolution test charts in the center and in each corner of the frame yielded a print which showed the left-front corner of the field to be somewhat brighter than the center. The left-rear and right-front corners were lighter than the center, and the right-rear corner was so low in illumination that the test chart in this corner failed to reproduce at all. At small lens apertures, other effects of unevenness also occurred. All the test charts in the corners were partially cut off because of the rounded corners of the lower glass flat.

When the lens is used at maximum aperture there is a noticeable difference in sharpness between the center and the edges and corners. In printing a test negative from a newspaper page in which the size of the type face on the print was necessarily small because of the limited range of magnification of the Rollacopy, an aperture of f16 was required to achieve adequate sharpness at the edges of the image. The use of such a small aperture obliges the operator to use high speed materials and darkroom conditions if legible prints from finely detailed originals are to be obtained.

Summary

In view of the limitations and shortcomings exhibited by the Rollacopy tested, it cannot be considered a satisfactory reader-printer device for library use. It is by no means easy or convenient to use. If the microforms being reproduced are of the typewritten office records kind or printed materials of moderate size filmed at reduction ratios within the enlargement capabilities of the Rollacopy, and if darkroom space can be provided for its use so that high-speed photographic materials can be exposed at small lens apertures, it can be made to work. But in reproducing many typical microforms commonly found in library collections — microforms filmed at reduction ratios requiring a higher magnification than 12X for easy legibility, or microforms of materials having small type faces or fine details such as are common in scientific works — an operator can expect a good deal of difficulty and, in many cases, results which at best may not be satisfactory.

9 The Universel

General description

The Universel consists of three components — a microfilm reader, a glass-covered easel for holding a sheet of sensitized paper flat, and a stabilization processing unit. The Universel can be used to read or make prints from 16 mm. or 35 mm. roll microfilm and from microfiche. The microfilm reader is of a type commonly used in Europe, in which the image is projected upward to a slanting mirror which in turn projects the image downward to the reading or printing surface. Magnification is controlled by extending or shortening the position of the arms which support the mirror. The

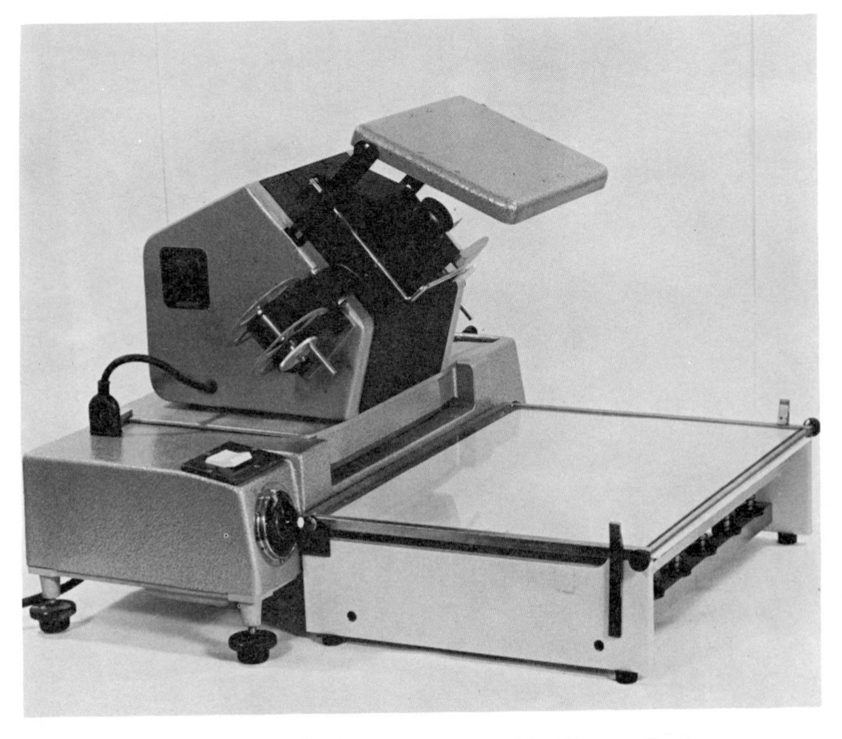

Fig. 34. The Universel. Mirror positioned for 7X magnification.

Fig. 35. The Universel. Mirror positioned for 10X magnification.

Universel is the only stabilization process reader-printer tested in which the manufacturer has provided an automatic replenishment system for maintaining the level of the developing and stabilizing solutions (Figure 36).

Specifications

Manufacturer: O. L. Beauvais.

Where manufactured: France.

Process employed: Stabilization.

Measurements: Width—24 inches. Depth—11½ inches (without easel). Height—21½ inches (with mirror arms at maximum extension). Weight—58 pounds. Easel width—18⅝ inches. Easel depth—14 inches. Easel height—5¾ inches (to top of clamps).

Size of printing surface: 12½ by 16 inches.

Size of mirror: 6¾ by 6¾ inches.

Lens: Make—Boyer "Saphir B." Focal length—50 mm. Aperture—Maximum: f3.5; minimum: f3.5. Magnification—Three fixed magnifications of 7X, 9X, and 10X when easel is used. By raising or lowering easel, intermediate or higher magnifications can be obtained. Image sizes—7X: 8⅛ by 11¾ inches; 9X: 10⅞ by 15⅝ inches; 10X: 12⅛ by 17¾ inches.

Focusing method: Helical mount.

Power requirements: The unit is equipped with a transformer which permits operation on line loads of 110, 125, 145, 220, and 245-volt 50/60 cycle, alternating current.

Electrical components: 8-volt Phillips projection lamp; transformer; exposure timer; lamp rheostat; processing unit drive motor.

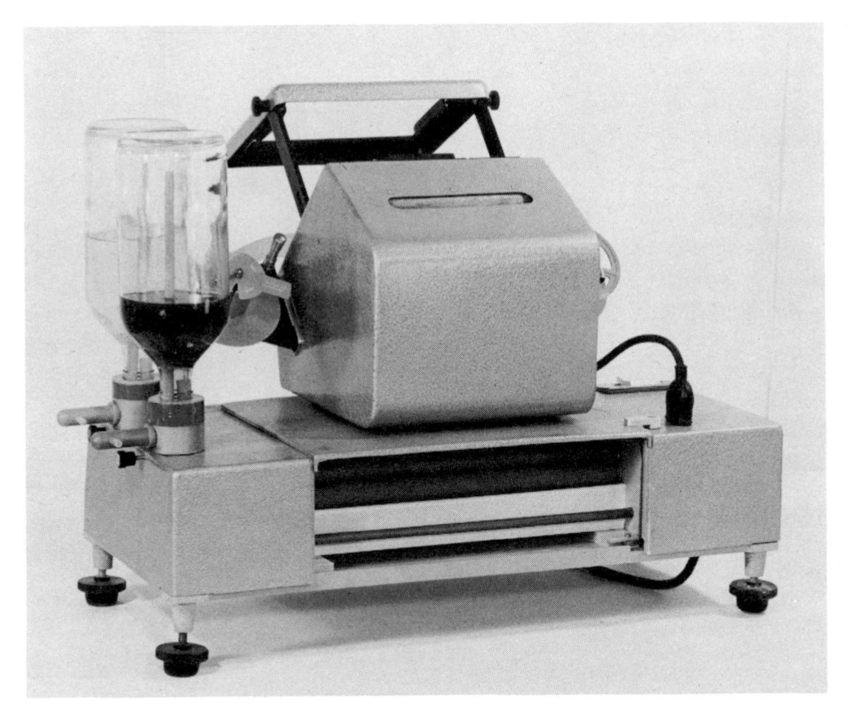

Fig. 36. Supply bottles for automatically maintaining correct solution level.

Construction: Processing section—Cast metal base on four screw-threaded legs for leveling; cast metal cover; rubber-covered stainless steel rollers; nylon gears; two compartment plastic solution tray. Projection assembly—Cast metal base; sheet metal lamp house; sheet metal lens mount and mirror assembly. Easel—Plastic sides supported by metal cross members. Plastic easel base supported by 12 compression springs and covered with foam rubber; plate-glass easel cover in metal frame; locking clamps at both sides.

Film-transport assembly: Capacity—100-foot rolls of 16 mm. or 35 mm. microfilm. Spindles—1:1 ratio on ⅝-inch turning radius.

Flats—Upper and lower flats mounted in removable metal plates for cleaning. Upper flat can be separated from lower flat by means of spring-loaded lever when film is being advanced.

Processor: Tray capacity—Developer: 16 ounces; stabilizer: 22 ounces. Width—12 inches. Maximum print size accommodated —11 to 11½ inches by any length. Drive—Nylon gear train.

Maintenance: Glass flats, lens, mirror, and easel glass should be kept clean. When chemicals are changed, tray, rollers, and replenisher supply bottles should be washed with warm water, drained, and reassembled.

Cost of machine: $475 (plus duty and shipping costs).

Warranty: Unstated.

Operation

The first step in setting up the Universel is to level the easel and then level the base of the processor by means of the four screw-threaded feet. As shown in Figure 37, the processing section consists of a base on which the drive motor is mounted, a two-compartment plastic tray, the roller assembly, and a cover. The roller assembly is mounted over the tray (Figure 38) with the roller gears meshed with the drive motor gear. The roller assembly is securely locked in place by means of two movable arms located at the front and back of the left-hand end of the assembly. The solution bottles can then be installed and locked in place with set screws, and the projection unit placed on top of the processing section, locked in place, and plugged into the outlet provided (Figure 39).

A reel of microfilm can then be placed on the right-hand spindle. The film is then positioned against the lower glass flat by lifting the "U" shaped lever which supports the upper glass flat, and the leader end of the film threaded into the take-up reel at the left.

The operation of the projection lamp and the processing-section drive motor is controlled by means of a pair of bascule buttons located above the exposure timing device. With the easel in position and the projection lamp turned on, the lever which lifts the upper glass flat is raised and the film advanced to the desired frame. The mirror can then be adjusted to the desired magnification and optimum angle, and the image brought into focus by rotating the lens. Exposure can be controlled in two ways: the duration of the exposure can be controlled by means of the automatic exposure timer which is scaled in 1-second divisions over a range of from 0 to 60 seconds; the intensity of the projection lamp can be controlled by means of the rheostat located behind the left-hand film spindle which is marked in divisions from 0 to 100. The choice of lamp intensity and exposure interval will depend on the background density of

Fig. 37. Base, solution tray, roller assembly, and cover of the processing section of the Universel.

the negative being printed, the degree of magnification, and the speed of the sensitized paper being used.

When an exposure setting has been determined, a sheet of sensitized paper is placed in the proper position under the easel glass and the glass locked securely in place. The exposure is then made and the exposed sheet removed from the easel and inserted in the opening at the front of the processing section (Figure 39) and then removed from the back of the processing section as it emerges (Figure 40). Since both the front and back of the unit must be accessible to the operator, the unit should be mounted on a table which will provide such access.

The spring-pressure construction of the easel of the Universel permits it to be used also as a contact reflex copier. An original document and a sheet of sensitized material can be placed in the easel where the spring pressure holds them in firm contact and the exposure made by means of the projection lamp.

Analysis

The performance of the Universel was adversely affected by one serious fault in particular in the optical system; the lens is not parallel to the film plane. The error is so great that it can readily be seen merely by looking at the profile of the machine. Consequently, when an image is projected onto the easel and the mirror adjusted to bring the projected image to rectilinear form, over-all sharpness of the image is impossible to achieve. The image is (a) sharp in the center and blurred at both the front and back edges, or (b) sharp at the front edge only and increasingly blurred toward the back edge, or (c) sharp at the back edge and increasingly blurred toward the front edge.

Fig. 38. Roller assembly in position.

The definition of the lens in any area that is brought into focus is very good indeed, but the misalignment of the lens destroys whatever efficiency the lens might have. Undoubtedly, in the reproduction of many microtransparencies, the size of the characters of the text in the projected image would be great enough to be legible despite this misalignment, but in printing from microforms of finely detailed originals, or if, in the interests of convenience or economy, large originals were projected at a substantial reduction in size to meet the size limitations of the usually available photocopy papers, the misalignment of the lens with respect to the film plane would result in prints that would not be legible. Since the quality of the lens itself is quite good, it is unfortunate that its mounting in the machine was not done with the degree of precision which any good optical system necessarily requires.

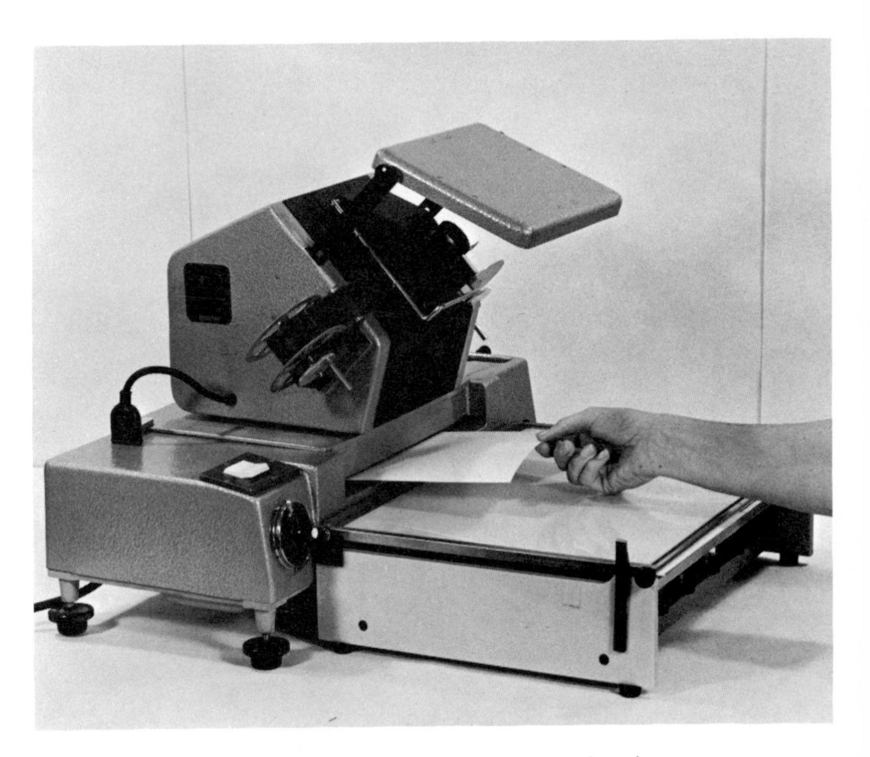

Fig. 39. Microfilm projection unit and easel in place.
Exposed sheet being fed into processing section.

Another fault in the optical system is the limitation imposed by the 50 mm. focal length of the lens. This focal length is sufficient to cover the area of the frame size produced on 35 mm. film having perforations on two edges. This frame measures 1 by 1½

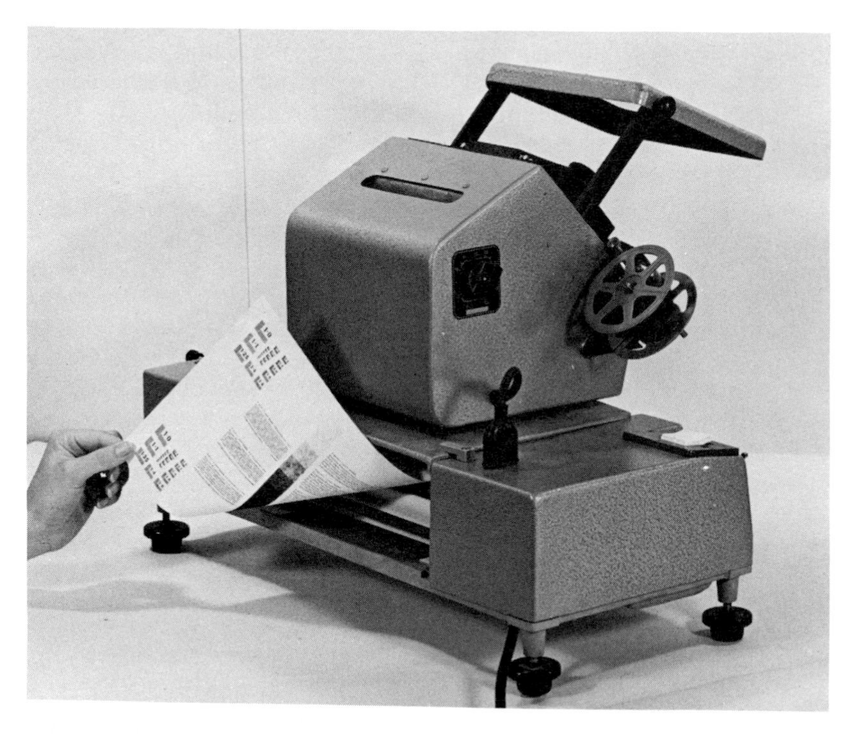

Fig. 40. Removing processed sheet as it emerges from processing section.

inches, and double-perforated film has long been popular in Europe. In this country, however, non-perforated film, which has a frame size of 1¼ by 1¾ inches, has for a long time been the accepted standard. A normal lens having a focal length of 50 mm. is simply not capable of producing a projected image of a frame as large as 1¼ by 1¾ inches which is sharp to the edges.

A third fault in the optical system was encountered in focusing the projected image. Focusing is done by rotating the lens in a helical mount. The angle of the helical threads, however, is so shallow that the lens must be turned several times before any appreciable change in focus is apparent. The process of moving the image into focus and out and back in again in locating the point where sharpness is at its optimum is thus a slow one.

Another factor which, if not attended to with care, will add still further to the problems of achieving a reasonably sharp image occurs in levelling the machine so that the base of the processor unit, which supports the projector assembly, is perfectly parallel to the surface of the printing easel. The base of the processor unit is equipped with four legs which have screw threads. The feet of the easel do not have any similar adjustment. The level of the easel must therefore be checked first and the reader-processor unit then brought to the same plane by adjusting the height of the screw legs. Also, when searching through a 100-foot roll of film for particular frames, the exceedingly small turning radius of the film spindles makes the operation a very slow one.

The sensitized material and solutions supplied by the manufacturer go under the trade name of Dalco "Dalcopy" and are manufactured in The Netherlands by The Nederlandsche Fotographische Industrie, N.V. However, more readily available papers of appropriate speed for use with the Universel can be substituted, such as the Polyclair line available from dealers who handle Polymicro equipment; Rollacopy paper, available from the Andrews Paper and Chemical Company and Rollacopy dealers; and Fotorite papers available through Fotorite dealers. If any of these brands of paper are used in the Universel, the manufacturer's developer and stabilizer solutions should also be used. In any event, regardless of which brands of paper and chemicals are used, the determination of the correct exposure interval for any given microfilm negative or positive will be a matter of trial and error. Negatives of high density will, of course, require longer exposures than those of lower density. For any given negative, the exposure will be longer if the magnification is high than it will be if the magnification is low. Waste due to incorrect exposures is therefore bound to occur.

Summary

As was brought out in the "Analysis," the Universel which was tested exhibited too many faults in the design and construction of its optical system to rate any kind of favorable recommendation. But, even if the misalignment of the lens were corrected, the focusing method improved, and the focal length of the lens increased, the difficulties an operator would encounter in dealing with problems such as magnification control and exposure determination still rank as serious drawbacks in terms of the kind of simplicity and efficiency needed by the librarian or the scholar. Even an improved model, however, is, as a printer, merely a photographic enlarging device to which a stabilization processor has been added, and not a very efficient photographic enlarger at that.

Any of a number of photographic enlargers used with stabilization processing could exceed the performance of the Universel and compare favorably in price, were it not for the fact that relatively few enlargers are equipped to handle film in 100-foot rolls. This, however, in many cases, could be done relatively easily and inexpensively. As a reader or as a reader-printer for the production of prints from the general run of library microforms, the Universel exhibits severe shortcomings and limitations which disqualify it for this purpose.

10 The Microcard Copier Type I

General description

The Microcard Copier Type I is a device which has been designed to produce automatically an enlarged, positive copy of a page of text from a Microcard. The diffusion-transfer-reversal process is used to produce a positive print from the positive image of a Microcard. The machine is not a true reader-printer since it does not have a screen for reading an enlarged image of the Microcard being projected. It has, instead, an eyepiece for viewing the Microcard in order to locate and position the desired page for printing. With a

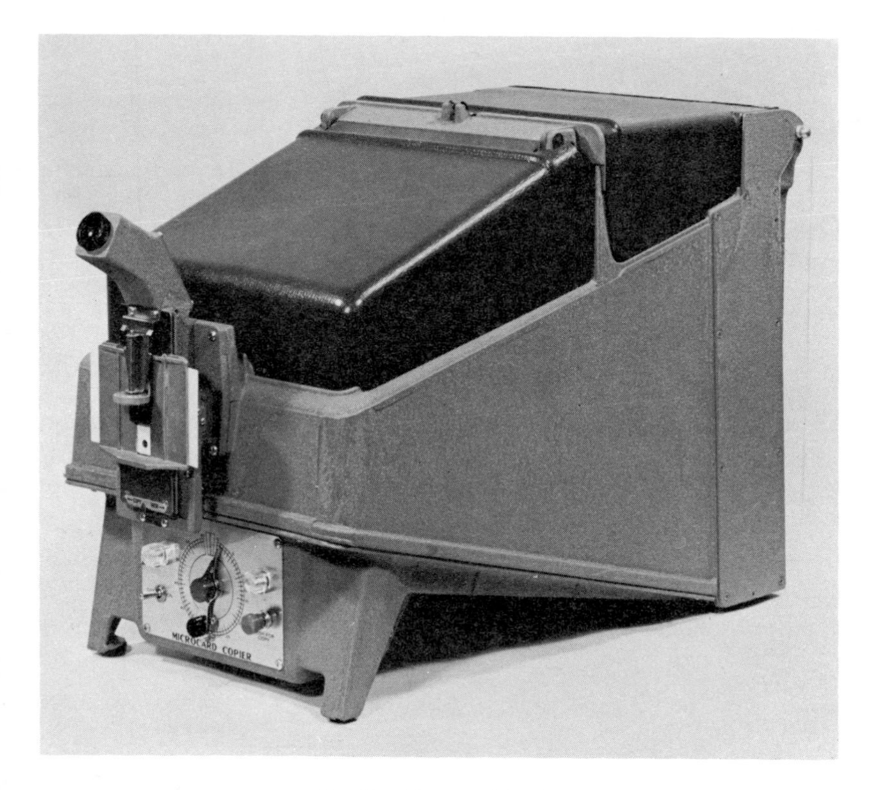

Fig. 41. Microcard Copier.

Microcard in position for printing, pressing a button starts the copying cycle. The finished print emerges in approximately 45 seconds.

Specifications

Manufacturer: Microcard Reader Corporation.

Where manufactured: United States.

Process employed: Diffusion-transfer-reversal.

Measurements: Width—13½ inches. Depth—29 inches. Height—17 inches. Weight—71 pounds.

Size of print: 8½ by 13 inches.

Size of image on print: 8¼ by 10 inches.

Size of roll stock copy paper: 8½ inches by 98 feet.

Cost per roll: Negative—$5.98; Positive—$4.78; total per set—$10.76.

Lens: Focal length—14 mm. Maximum aperture—f3.5. Magnification—19.5X.

Focusing method: Fixed focus.

Power requirements: 120 volts; 250 watts, 50/60 cycles.

Electrical components: Electronic exposure timer; indicator lamps; heating element; 3 drive motors; 9-watt projection lamp; fuse.

To replace lamp: The lamp is of a ring-type design and has a rated life of 3,000 hours. Should it become necessary to replace the lamp, the entire front assembly — lamp, card carrier, and eyepiece — must be replaced with a new assembly supplied by the manufacturer.

Construction: Cast metal housing; plastic covers; plastic solution tray; stainless steel wire feed guides; rubber-covered stainless steel rollers; stainless steel paper compartment covers.

Maintenance: At the end of each day the activator should be siphoned off, the solution tray and feed guides washed with warm water, and the rollers cleaned with a damp sponge.

Cost of machine: $950.

Warranty: Six-month warranty on all parts except the lamp. This warranty is based on the assumption that the machine will be given reasonable care and will not be tampered with by unauthorized personnel.

Operation

The machine must first be loaded with a roll of negative and a roll of positive diffusion-transfer-reversal paper, and the solution tray in the processing section must be filled with developer. A Microcard is then inserted in a card holder. This card holder is equipped with a rubber wheel which is rotated to control the horizontal positioning of the image. The card-holder assembly can be moved up and down for vertical positioning. Behind the card holder is a sliding mask which is moved to the right to view the Microcard and to the left when a copy is to be made. With the switch on and the mask in the viewing position, the Microcard can be examined though the eyepiece and then moved horizontally and vertically until the desired page is in view. To make a copy, the mask is moved to the copying position, the exposure timer is set, and the print button pushed. Approximately 30 to 45 seconds later, depending upon the exposure, the front cover can be raised and the negative and positive sheets removed. After a few seconds pause for completion of image transfer, the sheets can then be separated.

Analysis

The Microcard Copier which was submitted for testing exhibited a number of faults in its construction which had to be remedied by the manufacturer before testing could be done.

The trimmer blade which sheers the exposed print from roll paper stock was defective and failed to cut the paper all the way through. A replacement blade was sent but this was not finished to the same tolerances as the original blade and hence could not be installed. Finally, the chief engineer of the Microcard Reader Corporation installed an entirely new trimmer assembly but this assembly was not finished to the correct tolerances either; when it was installed it caused the paper advance rollers to separate. This was adjusted by relocating one screw hole. At the same time a heating element was installed to keep the humidity of the paper low enough so that it would advance properly. The machine was then finally ready to be tested.

The lens with which the Microcard Copier is equipped is capable of producing a very sharp projected image, but the actual image on a print can only be as sharp as the image on the Microcard itself. The largest single cause of partial illegibility in prints was this lack of clarity and definition in numerous Microcard images. This was especially true in printing from Microcards involving mathematical symbols, footnotes, subscript and superscript numbers, and other fine details. The problem was accentuated by the fact that the field of illumination which the ring-type lamp provides is not perfectly even. It is somewhat brighter in the center than in the corners. The degree of unevenness in terms of actual light output is relatively small, but is exaggerated by the very high contrast of the diffusion-transfer-reversal paper used in printing. The larger the size of the Microcard image, the more pronounced these effects become and, in many cases, no single exposure could be used to produce a print which was legible both in the center and in the corners. With smaller size Microcard images, the effects were less marked, but exposures, nonetheless, were still very critical if a fully legible print was to be achieved.

Another minor fault exhibited by the machine was an occasional failure in the exposure timing device. Prints made at identical settings were sometimes markedly different in appearance and in legibility.

Summary

The lack of standardization and control in the manufacture of some of the component parts used in the Microcard Copier points to the likelihood of different machines performing in a different manner, some exhibiting faults not present in others and some performing better than others. The three major faults which will affect the performance of all machines built according to the present design are: (a) the unevenness of the field of illumination; (b) the excessive contrast of the DTR paper employed; and (c) most important of all, variations in the clarity and quality of the Microcard images themselves. Because of these faults, prints from finely detailed originals may often be unsatisfactory and may involve extensive waste in trial-and-error attempts to establish an exposure time which will produce an optimum result.

In view of the need for a device which will produce an enlarged copy from a micro-opaque image, the Microcard Copier, despite its drawbacks, might still prove useful in certain applications where the Microcarded material does not involve fine details. Microcards of typescript reports, for example, can usually be reproduced in a legible fashion and with a greater tolerance for errors in exposure because of the boldness of the type face. But apart from the question of the quality of the Microcard images themselves — a problem which cannot be solved by any printing device — the faults in the machine preclude the possibility of a favorable recommendation at this time. It is to be hoped that the manufacturer will continue not only to improve this device but will also improve the quality of the Microcards themselves so that better prints can be made from them.

11 The Ross Microreader

General description

The Ross Microreader is the only one of the eight reader-printers tested that is capable of handling all of the microforms currently in use in libraries — Microcards, Microlex, Microprint, microfiche, and roll and strip microfilm in 35 mm. and 16 mm. widths.

In order to project an image from either transparent or opaque microforms, two light sources are provided — one in a housing at the top of the unit for illuminating microtransparencies and another within the unit for illuminating the surface of micro-opaques. The image is projected downward to a tilted mirror which reflects the image to a mirror at the back of the unit and thence to the viewing screen.

Specifications

Manufacturer: Ross, Limited.

Where manufactured: London, England.

Process employed: Optional (see "Analysis").

Measurements: Width—8 inches. Depth—13 inches. Height—17 inches to top of lamp house. Weight—22¼ pounds.

Size of screen: 6 by 7 inches.

Size of print: 6½ by 8½ inches.

Size of image on print: 6 by 7 inches.

Lenses available: Magnification—10X, 15X, and 18X. For certain types of laboratory work, microscope objectives of 27X and 37X are supplied.

Focusing method: Helical mount.

Power requirements: Either 200-250 volt or 100-130 volt operation with adjustments within these ranges to suit local requirements. Maximum current consumption—24 watts.

Electrical components: Transformer; projection lamp.

Construction: Cast metal.

Film-transport assembly: Capacity—100-foot rolls of 16 mm. or

35 mm. microfilm. Spindles—1:1 ratio on ½-inch radius. Flats—Lower glass flat fixed. Upper glass flat movable. Glass flats are separated by finger pressure on upper flat. Film-transport assembly can be revolved 90 degrees. Sheet film and micro-opaque carriers—3- by 5-inch glass flats for Microcards and 7.5- by 12.5-cm. microfiche; 6½- by 8½-inch glass flats for larger micro-opaques.

Maintenance: Dust should be removed from mirrors with camel's-hair brush. Glass flats and glass plate of photographic attachment should be cleaned with soap and warm water, and dried with lint-free cloth. Lenses should be cleaned with lens tissue or camel's-hair brush.

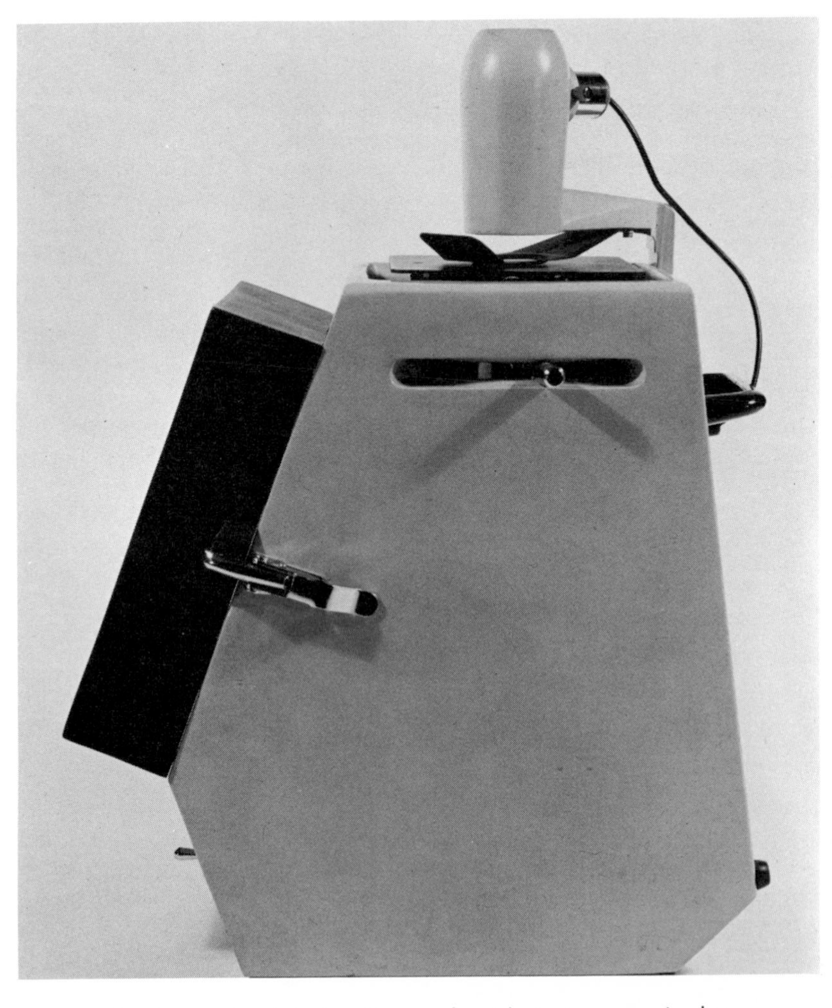

Fig. 42. Profile of the Ross Microreader with viewing screen in place.

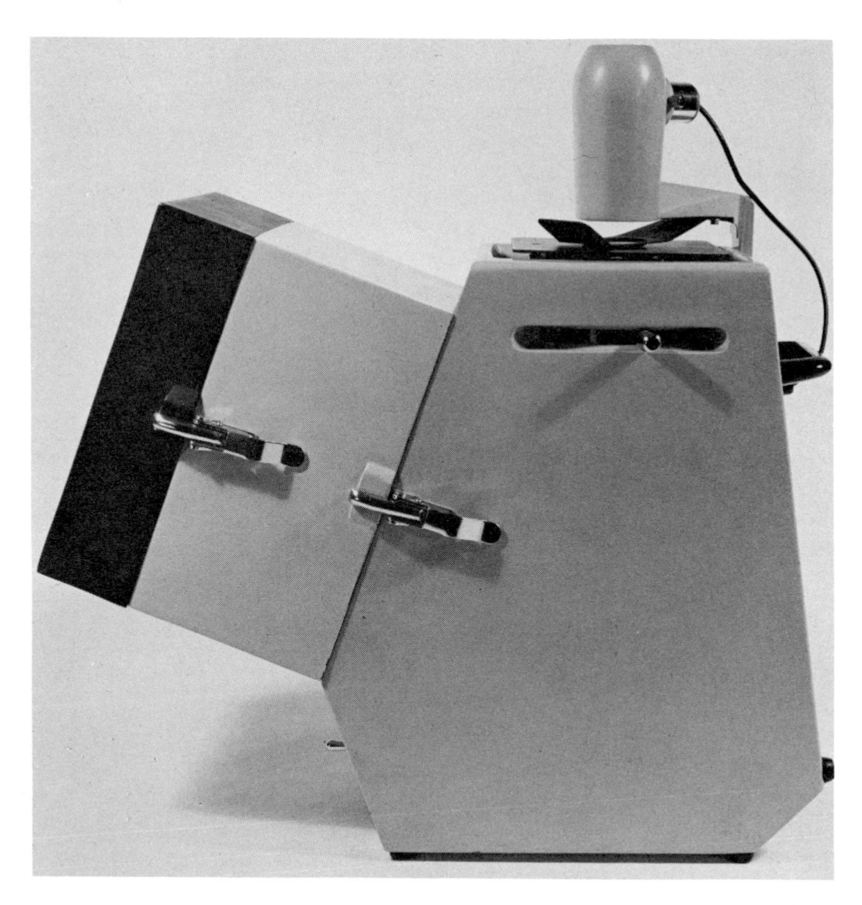

Fig. 43. Profile of the Ross Microreader with screen extension unit in place for increasing the magnification to 18X.

Costs:

Reader, with 15X lens and two 3- by 5-inch glass plates for reading Microcards or microfiche	$220.50
35 mm. and 16 mm. combined microfilm holder with 35 mm. and 16 mm. take-up reels	26.60
10X lens—an alternative lens for use mainly with 35 mm. microfilm and larger images	21.70
Screen extension unit to increase the magnification from 15X to 18X	8.82
Extension arm and two 6½- by 8½-inch glass plates for reading Microprint or Microlex records	7.14
Photographic attachment with focusing screen for 6½- by 8½-inch photographic paper	27.30
Carrying case and accessory box for reader, 3- by 5-inch glass	

plates, 4 spare lamps, 10X or 15X lens, 6½- by 8½-inch glass plates, extension arm and screen extension unit.....	15.40
Carrying case for two 35 mm./16 mm. microfilm holders, two 16 mm. adapters, 1 set of spare glasses and two 100-foot, 35 mm. reels	14.35
Carrying case for photographic attachment................	12.95
27X or 37X microscope objectives................	Price on request

Costs of spare or replacement parts are as follows:

Lamps (11 volt, 12 watt)	$ .68
3- by 5-inch glass plates, per pair.........................	.70
6½- by 8½-inch glass plates, per pair......................	1.05
Standard 15X lens	43.40
Glass plate for photographic attachment..................	1.33
Focusing screen for photographic attachment..............	1.47
Glass viewing screen	30.10
Back mirror	7.00
Bottom mirror	6.30
Glass plates for 35 mm. film carrier, per set................	8.82
16 mm. adapters (2) for microfilm holder..................	.70

Warranty: Unstated.

Operation

When used as a reader or as a reader-printer, convenience of use varies considerably among the different microforms. Microcards and microfiche are relatively easy to use. Reading from microfilm in roll form is considerably more awkward and difficult.

Microcards. To read from a Microcard, the card is placed between the two 3- by 5-inch glass plates and then placed in a face-down position under the spring clip beneath the lamp housing (Figures 44 and 45). With the right-hand switch in a "down" position for micro-opaques, the left-hand "on-off" switch is turned on to illuminate the image. Preliminary focusing can be done from any portion of the card by moving the metal arm at the upper-right side (Figure 44) backward or forward. The Microcard can then be positioned for the desired page by moving the glass flats manually until the page is located and positioned on the viewing screen. Focusing can then be done for optimum legibility.

Microfiche. A microfiche is placed between the two 3- by 5-inch glass flats and positioned on the reader in the same manner as a Microcard — i.e., with the "right-reading" side of the microfiche placed downward. The right-hand switch is turned to the "up" position for illuminating microtransparencies. The projected image can then be brought into focus and positioned.

Microlex and Microprint. To read Microlex and Microprint,

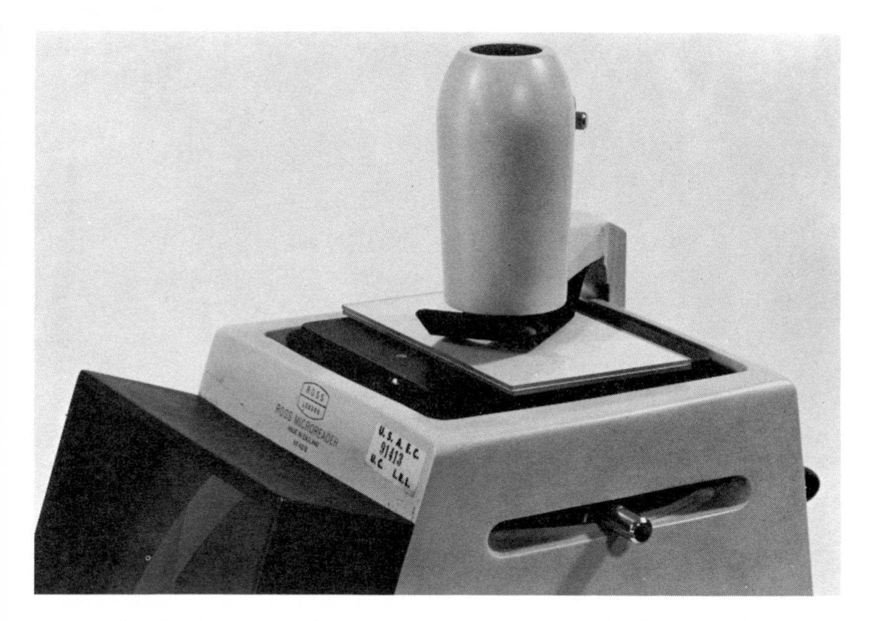

Fig. 44. A Microcard between glass flats in place under the spring clip.

the lamp house is first detached by unplugging the jack at the rear of the reader and removing one knurled screw which holds the lamp house in place. The extension arm which is used to hold Microlex and Microprint sheets flat is fastened into position with the knurled screw which held the lamp house in place. A Microlex or Microprint sheet is then placed between 6½- by 8½-inch glass flats and positioned on the reader beneath the spring clip of the extension arm. With the image in focus, the glass flats are moved in or out and from side to side until the desired page is located.

Roll microfilm. A separate film holder is supplied for reading 35 mm. or 16 mm. microfilm in roll form. As shown in Figure 46, it consists of a circular metal frame which holds the lower glass flat, a separate upper glass flat, and two arms for the spindles on which film reels are placed. Reels of 35 mm. film are held in place on the spindles by means of a hinged catch. A supplementary collar is used to hold 16 mm. reels in place.

A reel of 35 mm. microfilm is placed on the left-hand spindle and the film leader strip attached to a take-up reel on the right-hand spindle. Because of the design of the optical system, negative microfilms must be mounted on the spindles with the emulsion side of the film facing up. The upper glass flat is then placed on top of the film and the entire assembly inserted under the spring clip below the lamp housing (Figure 47). The octagonal-shaped upper glass flat is bevelled on each end and has highly polished rounded

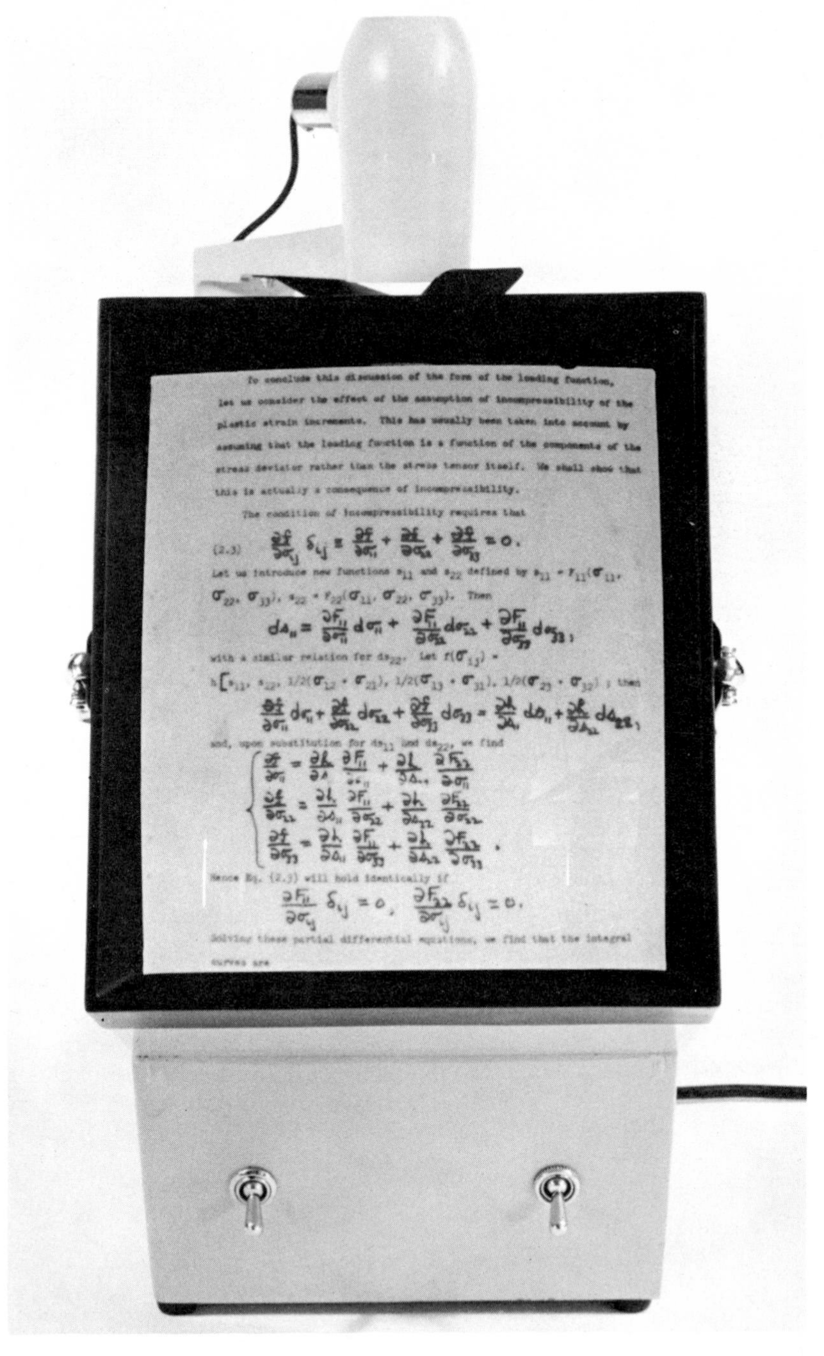

To conclude this discussion of the form of the loading function, let us consider the effect of the assumption of incompressibility of the plastic strain increments. This has usually been taken into account by assuming that the loading function is a function of the components of the stress deviator rather than the stress tensor itself. We shall show that this is actually a consequence of incompressibility.

The condition of incompressibility requires that

$$\frac{\partial f}{\partial \sigma_{ij}} \delta_{ij} = \frac{\partial f}{\partial \sigma_{11}} + \frac{\partial f}{\partial \sigma_{22}} + \frac{\partial f}{\partial \sigma_{33}} = 0. \tag{2.3}$$

Let us introduce new functions s_{11} and s_{22} defined by $s_{11} = F_{11}(\sigma_{11}, \sigma_{22}, \sigma_{33})$, $s_{22} = F_{22}(\sigma_{11}, \sigma_{22}, \sigma_{33})$. Then

$$ds_{11} = \frac{\partial F_{11}}{\partial \sigma_{11}} d\sigma_{11} + \frac{\partial F_{11}}{\partial \sigma_{22}} d\sigma_{22} + \frac{\partial F_{11}}{\partial \sigma_{33}} d\sigma_{33},$$

with a similar relation for ds_{22}. Let $f(\sigma_{ij}) = h[s_{11}, s_{22}, 1/2(\sigma_{12} + \sigma_{21}), 1/2(\sigma_{13} + \sigma_{31}), 1/2(\sigma_{23} + \sigma_{32})]$; then

$$\frac{\partial f}{\partial \sigma_{11}} d\sigma_{11} + \frac{\partial f}{\partial \sigma_{22}} d\sigma_{22} + \frac{\partial f}{\partial \sigma_{33}} d\sigma_{33} = \frac{\partial h}{\partial s_{11}} ds_{11} + \frac{\partial h}{\partial s_{22}} ds_{22},$$

and, upon substitution for ds_{11} and ds_{22}, we find

$$\begin{cases} \dfrac{\partial f}{\partial \sigma_{11}} = \dfrac{\partial h}{\partial s_{11}} \dfrac{\partial F_{11}}{\partial \sigma_{11}} + \dfrac{\partial h}{\partial s_{22}} \dfrac{\partial F_{22}}{\partial \sigma_{11}} \\ \dfrac{\partial f}{\partial \sigma_{22}} = \dfrac{\partial h}{\partial s_{11}} \dfrac{\partial F_{11}}{\partial \sigma_{22}} + \dfrac{\partial h}{\partial s_{22}} \dfrac{\partial F_{22}}{\partial \sigma_{22}} \\ \dfrac{\partial f}{\partial \sigma_{33}} = \dfrac{\partial h}{\partial s_{11}} \dfrac{\partial F_{11}}{\partial \sigma_{33}} + \dfrac{\partial h}{\partial s_{22}} \dfrac{\partial F_{22}}{\partial \sigma_{33}} . \end{cases}$$

Hence Eq. (2.3) will hold identically if

$$\frac{\partial F_{11}}{\partial \sigma_{ij}} \delta_{ij} = 0, \quad \frac{\partial F_{22}}{\partial \sigma_{ij}} \delta_{ij} = 0.$$

Solving these partial differential equations, we find that the integral curves are

Fig. 45. Screen image of a Microcard at a magnification of 18X.

edges at each side. Finger pressure applied to one of the bevelled ends causes the upper flat to tilt and separate from the lower flat, thus providing room for advancing the film without the danger of scratching the emulsion surface (Figure 48). Because the roll-film holder is held in position merely by the pressure of the spring clip, it can be positioned back and forth and from side to side or can be rotated 90 degrees if needed (Figure 49).

Fig. 46. The microfilm holder.

Photographic attachment. The photographic attachment consists of a cast metal frame which holds a sheet of glass and a pressure platen. To make an enlarged print of the projected image of a microform, the reader screen is removed and replaced with the photographic attachment (Figure 50). For focusing the image, a 2- by 2-inch square of glass having one frosted surface is placed against the surface of the glass screen of the photographic attachment with the frosted side inward (Figure 51). When the image has been properly focused, a sheet of 6½- by 8½-inch photographic paper is placed against the glass plate (Figure 52) and covered with the pressure platen (Figure 53) which is locked in place by means of a clamp at the bottom of the unit (Figure 54). The paper is exposed by turning on the "on-off" switch for the required time interval. When ordinary photographic materials are employed, the resultant print is negative and reverse-reading. Positive prints can

Fig. 47. The microfilm holder in position for reading.

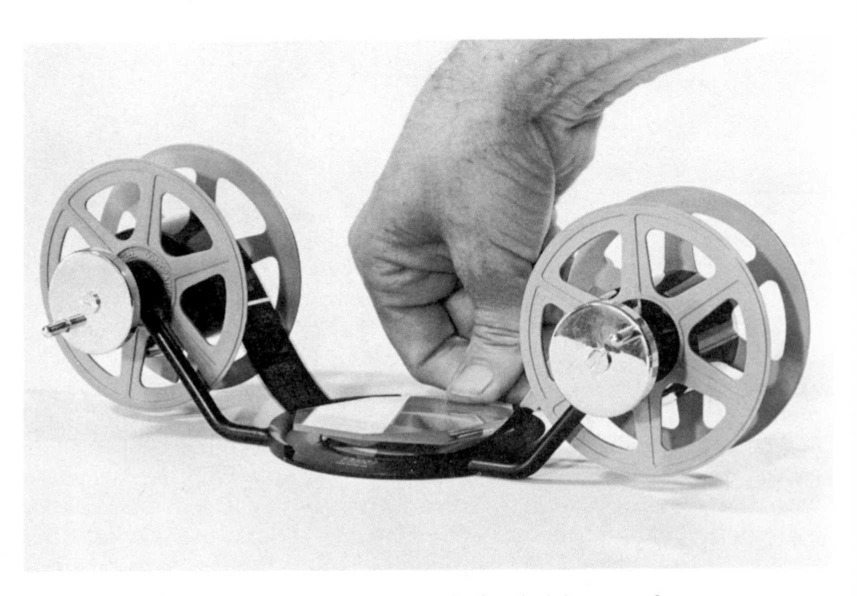

Fig. 48. Depressing the bevelled end of the upper flat to separate it from the lower flat.

be made by the direct contact method by using the photographic attachment as a contact printing frame.

Analysis

Construction. The quality of construction and finish appeared, on the whole, to be very good. It was surprising, therefore, to find in the unit which was tested, that the lugs on the various accessories which are fastened to the unit by the toggle clamps on each side were not machined to a uniform size. This was conspicuous in two instances. When the reader screen is in place, the toggle clamp at the right side fits over its lug very loosely. If, in carrying the reader, it should become tipped to the right no more than 20 to 25 degrees, gravity alone is enough to cause the toggle clamp to become disengaged from the lug. Should this occur it is possible that the reader screen, which is quite heavy, may fall and become damaged or broken. In the second instance, it was found that when the photographic attachment is mounted on the screen extension unit it is quite impossible to close either one of the toggle clamps.

Fig. 49. Microfilm holder rotated 90 degrees.

Fig. 50. The photographic attachment.

Optical system. With both the 10X and 15X lenses, a slight unevenness in sharpness between the center and the corners was observed. If the center of the screen image is brought into sharp focus, the corners are slightly fuzzy. If focus at the corners is improved, sharpness at the center of the field falls off slightly. If a micro-image is simply to be read, this slight unevenness of focus is not a serious drawback since focus can be adjusted readily and the upper or lower portions of the page can be moved to the center of the screen where the image is both brightest and sharpest. In printing, however, this unevenness of focus frequently resulted in prints which were only partially legible or legible with difficulty.

The screen extension unit is used with the 15X lens to increase the magnification to 18X. It should be possible, therefore, to use it with the 10X lens to obtain an intermediate magnification of 13X. This is just possible with Microcards and microfiche, with the focusing lever at almost the limit of its forward throw. It is not possible with roll microfilm, where such a magnification might be most useful, because the thickness of the frame and lower glass flat of the microfilm holder raises the film plane just a little beyond the limit of the focusing device.

Illumination system. The brightness of the screen image was satisfactory, but only if the user's line of sight was on an axis close to perpendicular to the center of the screen. If the screen is at a slight angle to the user's line of sight, or if he shifts his head a few degrees off center, illumination falls off markedly. This effect is slightly less noticeable if the room where the reader is being used is darkened. The screen image of micro-opaques is much brighter than the screen image of microtransparencies.

The field of illumination of the projected image of a micro-

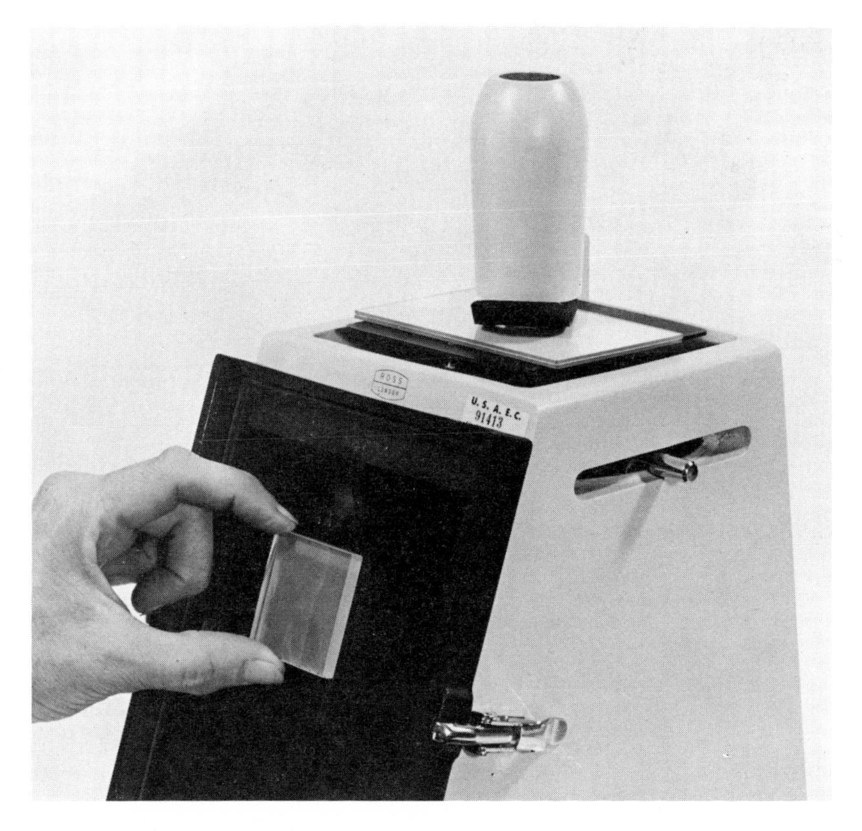

Fig. 51. Focusing the projected image by means of the focusing screen.

transparency is not even. The single condensing lens below the lamp is not adequate to spread the light evenly over the area covered by the lens. The field of illumination provided by the dual lamp system used for illuminating micro-opaques is also uneven, but not as markedly so as is the case with microtransparencies. With either microform, the degree of unevenness is in inverse proportion to the magnification. A slight falling off of illumination at the corners occurs at a magnification of 18X. A very marked unevenness occurs when a magnification of 10X is used. This is not a serious drawback if the image is projected on the screen simply to be read, because any portion of the image can be shifted to the center of the field where the image is brightest. But in making prints with the photographic attachment at magnifications of less than 18X, the unevenness of the field becomes very serious indeed.

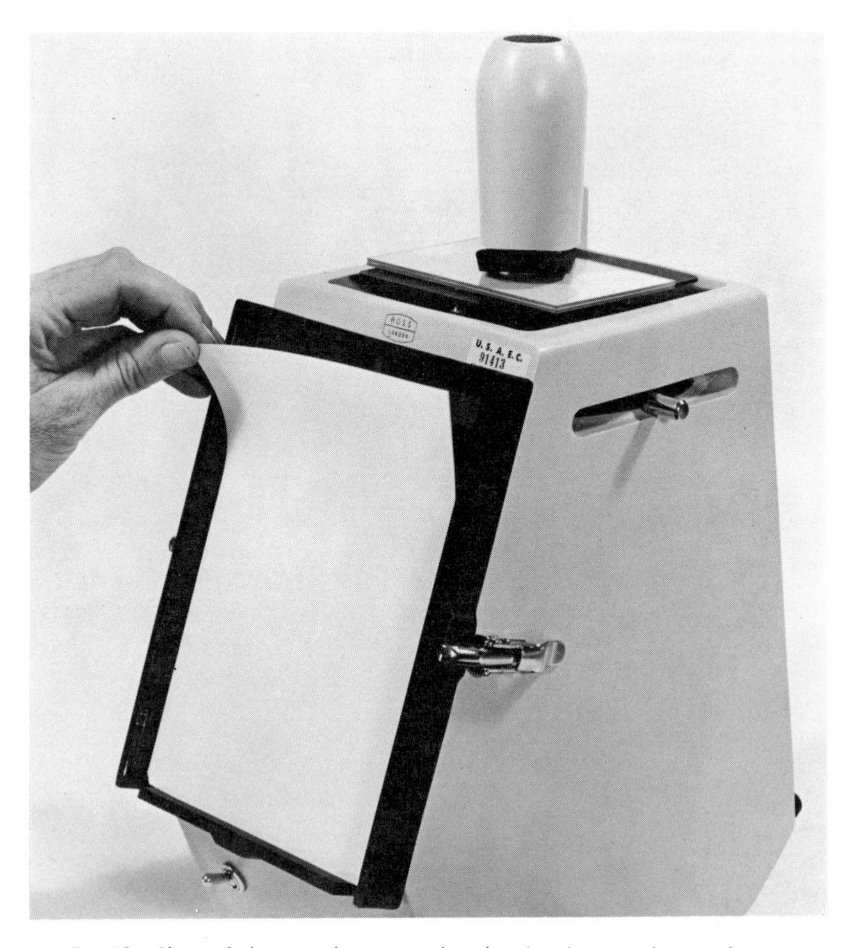

Fig. 52. Sheet of photographic paper placed in the photographic attachment.

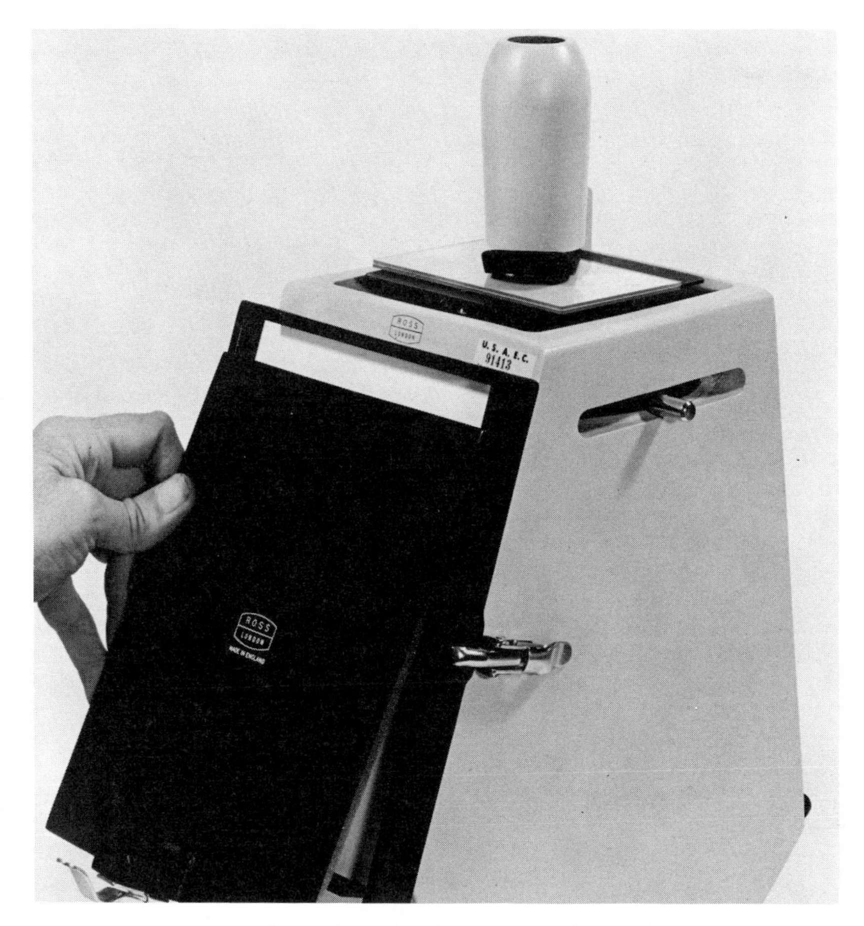

Fig. 53. Placing the cover of the photographic attachment over the photographic paper.

Screen size and magnification. The small screen size in relation to the magnifications available creates a number of problems for the user. If either dimension of the text of any original record is larger than the 6- by 7-inch screen, the entire text cannot be presented on the screen without some degree of reduction from original size. If any part of the original text is printed in a small type face or includes fine details such as reduced-size drawings, a reduction in size may impair legibility. This is especially true of Microcard or Microlex images which, in general, are not as clear and sharply defined as micro-images on film. Increasing the magnification will improve legibility but then only a portion of the text can be viewed. As long as the entire line *width* appears on the screen, reading convenience is satisfactory, but if a copy of the

Fig. 54. The cover of the photographic attachment locked in place for printing.

text is to be made by means of the photographic attachment, two or more prints will be required.

The problems encountered in working with fixed magnifications are common to all readers and reader-printers of this type. The basic difficulty stems from the fact that whereas the magnification ratios of the reader are fixed, the reduction ratios employed in the production of micro-images of various types of originals are not.

Depending upon the type of microform, reduction ratios ranging anywhere from 8 to 20 or more diameters are in common use. If, for example, pages of text 10 inches high must be reduced to ½ inch in height for presentation in the form of a Microcard or microfiche, a reduction ratio of 20 diameters will be required. If, on the other hand, such pages are copied on 35 mm. microfilm, a reduction ratio of only 8 diameters will suffice. In the first instance, the maximum magnification which the Ross Microreader is capable of—18X—is not great enough to provide a full-size image. In the second instance, the minimum magnification of 10X produces an image which is too large for the reader screen and which can only be read by shifting the image back and forth and up and down.

Problems with Microcards. At best the projected image of a Microcard is never truly clear and sharp on the reader screen, but this is in the nature of Microcards themselves — not a fault in the optical system of the reader. Film images are quite clear and sharp. The ordinary difficulty caused by the lack of true sharpness in the projected image of a Microcard is increased, however, by the smallness of the screen. At a magnification of 15X, many Microcarded images of printed materials and technical reports having pages measuring 8½ by 11 inches can be viewed in their entirety on the 6- by 7-inch screen but at a reduction in size from that of the original. If the screen extension unit is used to increase the magnification to 18X, the full width of the text is usually presented on the screen but not the full length. When the full width of the text barely fits the width of the screen, positioning becomes delicate and critical. Each manual movement of the card is magnified 18 times. Moving the card 1/16 inch causes a shift of the image of 1⅛ inches.

Problems with microfiche. Microfiche images on the reader screen, even when reduced in size, are usually much more easily read than Microcard images because of the superior sharpness of the film image. However, the delicacy with which critical positioning must be done at high magnifications is the same as it is with Microcards and is proportional to the magnification.

Problems with Microlex and Microprint. At 15X the full width of Microlex records of American Law Reports can be positioned on the reader screen but not quite the full length. Using the screen extension unit with the 10X lens to obtain a magnification of 13X brings the full length of the page into view, but this magnification is somewhat low for easy legibility.

Because the size and consequently the reduction ratio used in filming different types of originals for Micro-printing vary, the magnification required to present a legible image on the reader screen will vary also. For example, when using the 10X lens, Microprint images of sample pages from the Sabin *Bibliography* are easily legible. At 15X the full width but not the full length can be read. A full page from a sample Microprint sheet of the British *Sessional Papers* is, on the other hand, much too small to read at a magnification of 10X. At 15X, the full width of a page does not appear and portions of the text are still too small for easy legibility. At 18X, legibility is improved but only a portion of the page now appears on the viewing screen.

Problems with microfilm. Because of the limited area covered by the lens and the small size of the reader screen, the full width of 35 mm. film frames cannot be positioned on the reader screen, even at the lowest (10X) magnification. In addition to this limitation, certain inconveniences in the use of the microfilm holder were noted. Because the microfilm holder with its glass flats is much thicker than the two 3- by 5-inch flats supplied for Microcards or microfiche, the spring clip beneath the lamp house is forced into a higher position which results in pressure being applied by the spring clip at one point toward the rear. The pressure applied is adequate, but because pressure is at the rear it interferes with the elevation of the upper flat when pressure is applied to the front bevelled edge. Very strong finger pressure is required to depress the front bevelled edge. The alternative to this is to reach around or over the lamp house and reels and depress the bevelled edge at the rear of the upper flat with one hand while advancing the film with the other. As is shown in Figure 55, this is somewhat awkward and inconvenient to do.

As is shown in Figure 46, the cranks on the front of the film spindles are quite small. Cranking through the major portion of a 100-foot reel of microfilm with one hand while pressing down the rear bevelled edge of the upper glass flat becomes a rather lengthy and tedious business. Also, the process of cranking tends to make the microfilm holder skew, which makes spot scanning difficult.

Because of the lower reduction ratios commonly used in the production of micro-images in roll form, problems and limitations arising from the smallness of the size of the screen and the fixed magnification ratios available are likely to be more frequent and more acute in reading or printing from micro-images in roll form. To illustrate the nature of the problem with two practical examples, the text of a page from the *Unesco Bulletin for Libraries* is 7⅞ inches in height and the text of a page from *American Documentation* is 9¼ inches in height. If the basic 15X lens with which the reader is normally supplied is used, presentation of the full text of these pages on the screen of the reader requires a reduction ratio in filming of 17.2 for the former and 20 for the latter. If the reduction ratios used are lower, as is commonly the case with periodicals of these sizes, only a portion of the text appears on the screen. In order to minimize this difficulty, an accessory 10X lens

Fig. 55. Depressing the rear bevelled edge of the upper glass flat with one hand while advancing the film with the other.

is supplied but, even with the 10X lens, reduction ratios of 11.4 and 13.2 are required for the presentation of the full text of the two examples given. For reading, the most important criterion is that the reduction ratio is such that the full-line width of the text be visible on the screen. If the relationship between reduction ratio and magnification is such that the full-line width does not appear on the reader screen, the microfilm holder must then be shifted back and forth to read each line.

Problems in printing. By far the greatest number of drawbacks and limitations in the use of the Ross Microreader were encountered in using it as a reader-printer. The photographic attachment, which in itself is a well-constructed device, accepts photographic paper 6½ by 8½ inches in size. This is a standard size in England but is relatively uncommon in the United States. Papers for printing must therefore either be obtained by special order from paper manufacturers or cut from larger, readily available sizes such as 8 by 10 inches, 8½ by 11 inches (letter size), or 8½ by 13 inches, because a single cut would yield two 6½- by 8½-inch sheets without waste, but this, too, is a size not ordinarily stocked by photographic or photocopy supply houses.

A very considerable inconvenience in printing arises from the fact that the light output of both the illumination systems is quite low. If exposure times are to be kept within reason, highly sensitive papers must be used. Such papers cannot be handled under ordinary room light conditions or even under relatively dim illumination. For certain of the photographic papers which might be useful for printing, a room which can be completely darkened is needed. The choice, therefore, is either to isolate the reader in a room which can be darkened at will or take the reader to a darkroom whenever prints need to be made.

Three types of photographic materials can be used for making enlarged prints. The first of these includes a great variety of ordinary silver halide enlarging papers. The use of such materials requires, however, a photographic darkroom equipped for developing, fixing, washing, and drying the exposed prints. The second includes various kinds of high speed stabilization process materials such as Polyclair, Rollacopy, Dalcopy, Fotorite, etc. Exposed prints on these papers can be processed in a matter of seconds in small, compact, processing units such as Polymicro, the Fotorite, and various others. These processors eliminate the need for a sink, running water, and all of the paraphernalia needed for processing ordinary silver halide enlarging papers.

Ordinarily, the print resulting from the use of either of these two types of materials will be negative and reverse reading — a mirror image of what appears on the reader screen. To secure a right-reading positive, the reverse-reading negative must be recopied on a second sheet of photographic paper by the direct contact method. One method of avoiding this additional step is to use high speed stabilization emulsions coated on translucent instead of opaque supports. In exceptional cases, where the screen image is bold and clear, a very thin photographic paper may be employed to obtain a right-reading negative by placing it in the photographic attachment with the paper base instead of the emulsion surface facing the glass screen of the photographic attachment. Some loss of sharpness will ensue, since the projected image must pass through the paper base to reach the emulsion surface. A right-reading negative can also be made from transparent microforms by placing the microform over the lens in an upside-down position so that the screen image is reverse reading. This is relatively simple to do with microfiche but quite an awkward procedure with micro-images in roll form.

A method which enables the user to produce both a reverse-reading negative and a right-reading positive in a single step is by using a third type of material — high speed diffusion-transfer-reversal papers such as Gevaert GR. In this case the exposure is made on the negative sheet which can then be processed with a positive sheet in a small processing unit of the kind widely used for the copying of office records.

The use of high speed photographic papers involves another factor for which no provision is made in the design of the reader— exposure control. The advantages of obtaining a right-reading positive in a very rapid processing step when a DTR paper such as Gevaert GR paper is used are reduced somewhat by the fact that exposures from micro-opaques at a line voltage of 110 volts range between one-half and three-quarters of a second. This is too short an interval to control accurately when exposures are made by operating the "on-off" switch. Either a voltage-controlling device must be introduced into the circuit to reduce the light output or a highly accurate and sensitive exposure timing device must be added.

The making of prints from successive pages is made unnecessarily complicated by the fact that the focusing screen supplied with the photographic attachment is only 2 inches square. When a print from page one of an article has been made, the photographic attachment must be removed and replaced with the reader screen so that page two can be positioned for printing. The reader screen must then be removed and replaced with the photographic attachment for printing. If a focusing screen 6½ by 8 inches were used, these unnecessary changeovers from photographic attachment to screen and back again would be eliminated. Furthermore, in placing the 2-inch-square focusing screen on the glass surface of the photographic attachment, it is virtually impossible to keep from smudging the glass with finger prints.

The most serious problem in making prints was caused by the unevenness of the illumination systems, and was most acute in attempting to make prints from microtransparencies at the 10X magnification. The best prints were obtained at the maximum magnification of 18X where unevenness of illumination is least evident.

The problems caused by uneven illumination were further complicated by the fact that certain materials which potentially might be very useful for rapid print production, such as Gevaert GR, are high contrast materials which emphasize any unevenness of the field. A similar problem occurs if high contrast stabilization process papers or high contrast "wet process" silver halide papers are used. With papers such as these, any unevenness in illumination is strongly evident in the reverse-reading negative and still further exaggerated in the right-reading positive.

The reverse is true if low contrast papers are used. Such papers tend to minimize illumination differences and are well suited to the making of prints from microforms since most microforms have ample contrast. Diffusion-transfer-reversal papers for documentary reproduction purposes are high contrast materials, but low contrast materials for "wet processing" or stabilization processing are available. The use of such papers proved to be very helpful in partially overcoming the deficiencies in the illumination systems of the Ross Microreader. Furthermore, the use of low contrast materials effectively increases exposure latitude, thus reducing

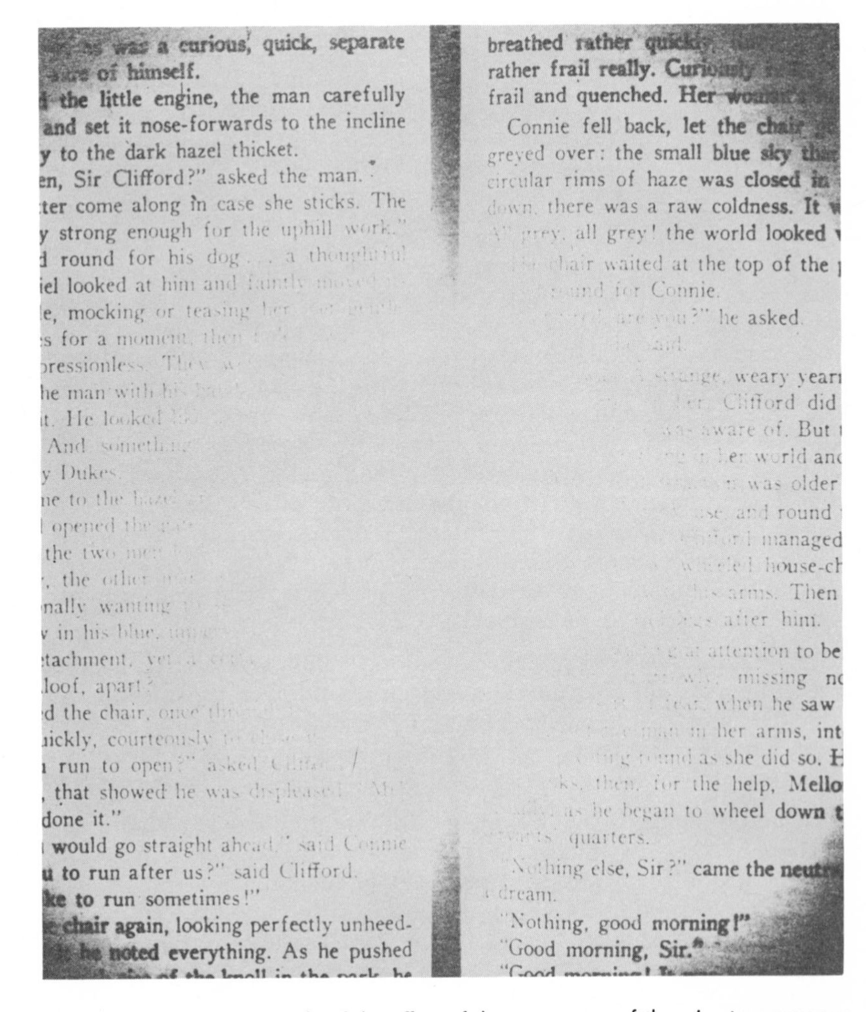

was a curious, quick, separate
of himself.
the little engine, the man carefully
and set it nose-forwards to the incline
y to the dark hazel thicket.
en, Sir Clifford?" asked the man.
ter come along in case she sticks. The
y strong enough for the uphill work."
d round for his dog . . . a thoughtful
iel looked at him and faintly
e, mocking or teasing
s for a moment, then
pressionless. They
he man with his
t. He looked
And something
y Dukes.
ne to the haze
opened the
the two men
, the other
nally wanting
in his blue,
tachment, yet
loof, apart?
d the chair, once
ickly, courteously
run to open?" asked Clifford
, that showed he was displeased
done it."
would go straight ahead," said Connie
u to run after us?" said Clifford.
ke to run sometimes!"
chair again, looking perfectly unheed-
he noted everything. As he pushed

breathed rather quickly
rather frail really. Curiously
frail and quenched. Her woman's
Connie fell back, let the chair
greyed over: the small blue sky that
circular rims of haze was closed in
down, there was a raw coldness. It w
All grey, all grey! the world looked
The chair waited at the top of the
round for Connie.
are you?" he asked.
said.
strange, weary year
Clifford did
was aware of. But
her world and
was older
and round
managed
house-ch
arms. Then
after him.
attention to be
missing n
when he saw
her arms, int
round as she did so. H
then, for the help, Mello
as he began to wheel down
quarters.
"Nothing else, Sir?" came the neutr
dream.
"Nothing, good morning!"
"Good morning, Sir."

Fig. 56. An extreme example of the effect of the unevenness of the microtransparency illumination system at a magnification of 10X when a high contrast paper (Gevaert GR) is used for printing.

waste caused by errors in exposure. The difference in the results obtained with high and low contrast materials are shown in Figures 56 and 57.

After testing a number of different materials, it was found that in terms of simplicity, speed, and economy, the best results were obtained by using low contrast stabilization process materials. The particular paper used was Polyclair Rapid, Contrast Grade No. 1. A Polymicro processing unit was used to process the exposed prints. Similar low contrast papers of other brands would, in all probability, yield similar results.

Exposures from a positive microtransparency were about ten

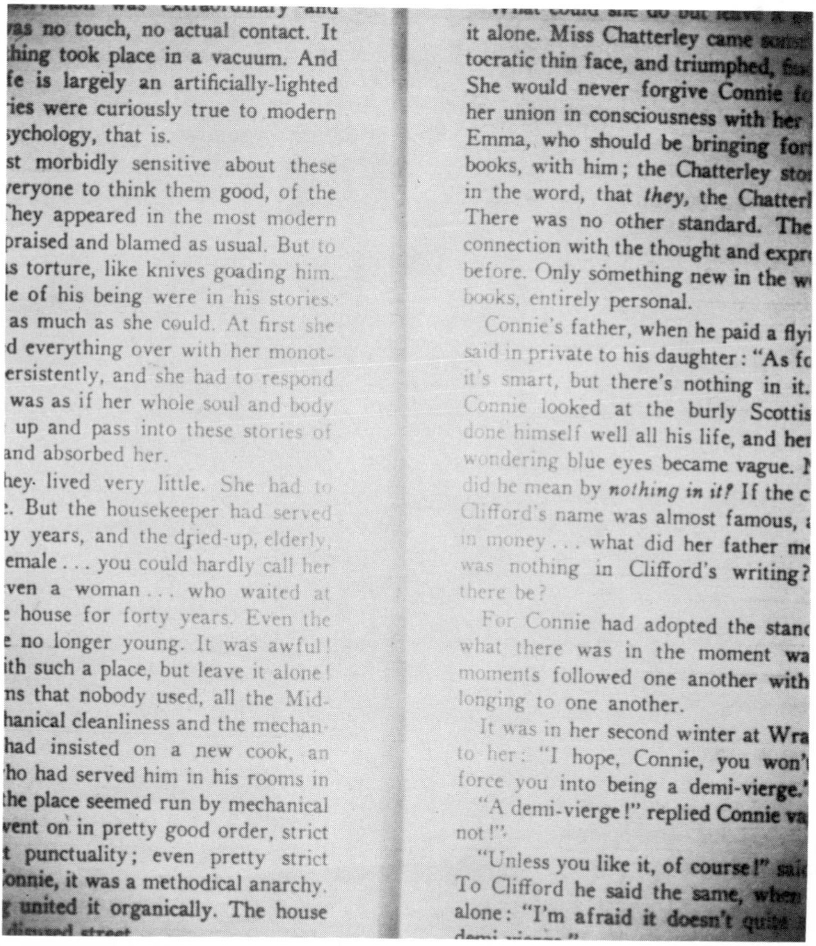
as no touch, no actual contact. It
hing took place in a vacuum. And
fe is largely an artificially-lighted
ies were curiously true to modern
ychology, that is.
st morbidly sensitive about these
eryone to think them good, of the
hey appeared in the most modern
praised and blamed as usual. But to
s torture, like knives goading him.
le of his being were in his stories.
as much as she could. At first she
d everything over with her monot-
ersistently, and she had to respond
was as if her whole soul and body
up and pass into these stories of
and absorbed her.
hey lived very little. She had to
. But the housekeeper had served
y years, and the dried-up, elderly,
emale . . . you could hardly call her
ven a woman . . . who waited at
e house for forty years. Even the
e no longer young. It was awful!
ith such a place, but leave it alone!
ns that nobody used, all the Mid-
hanical cleanliness and the mechan-
had insisted on a new cook, an
ho had served him in his rooms in
he place seemed run by mechanical
ent on in pretty good order, strict
t punctuality; even pretty strict
onnie, it was a methodical anarchy.
united it organically. The house

it alone. Miss Chatterley came
tocratic thin face, and triumphed,
She would never forgive Connie fo
her union in consciousness with her
Emma, who should be bringing fort
books, with him; the Chatterley sto
in the word, that *they*, the Chatterl
There was no other standard. The
connection with the thought and expr
before. Only something new in the w
books, entirely personal.

Connie's father, when he paid a flyi
said in private to his daughter: "As fo
it's smart, but there's nothing in it.
Connie looked at the burly Scottis
done himself well all his life, and her
wondering blue eyes became vague. N
did he mean by *nothing in it?* If the c
Clifford's name was almost famous, a
in money . . . what did her father me
was nothing in Clifford's writing?
there be?

For Connie had adopted the stand
what there was in the moment wa
moments followed one another with
longing to one another.

It was in her second winter at Wra
to her: "I hope, Connie, you won't
force you into being a demi-vierge."
"A demi-vierge!" replied Connie va
not!"
"Unless you like it, of course!" sai
To Clifford he said the same, when
alone: "I'm afraid it doesn't quite

Fig. 57. Reduction of the effects of uneven illumination at a magnification of 10X by using a low contrast paper (Polyclair Rapid, contrast grade No. 1).

seconds. Exposures from a Microcard were about two to three seconds which, although short, are still controllable when low contrast materials are used. Right-reading positives were made by placing a blank area of a Microcard over the lens where it could serve as a reflecting surface to illuminate the field of the photographic attachment. The reverse-reading negative was then placed against the glass of the photographic attachment with the image side forward, and covered with a sheet of the Polyclair low contrast paper. The printing exposure from the negative shown in Figure 57 was 35 seconds, but exposures as low as 25 seconds or as high as 45 seconds yielded legible copies.

While the deficiencies in the illumination systems can be overcome to some extent by the use of low contrast materials, the deficiencies in the optical system remain. In printing from microtransparencies it was usually possible to produce a print which, although fuzzy in some areas, was still legible. In printing from micro-opaques, however, the slight fuzziness of the micro-opaque itself plus the additional weakening of definition caused by the lens, often resulted in prints in which fine details were not legible.

Summary

As has been brought out in the rather detailed analysis of this machine, it falls far short of being an efficient reader-printer. When one considers the hand methods by which prints are made, in comparison with the more automated methods employed in the Filmac 100 or the Documat, it is perhaps unfair to class the Ross Microreader as a reader-printer. Nonetheless it is advertised as a device which is capable of performing the printing function. The manufacturer's intention of attempting to produce a device which could be used to read from all of the many existing types of library microforms is commendable. Also, in considering its versatility in this respect, the price is not excessive. But, from the standpoint of the user, versatility at a moderate purchase price is acquired at a considerable cost in convenience, especially when attempting to use the machine for reading 35 mm. microfilm. As a printing device, it exhibits far too many shortcomings to be favorably recommended.

12 Miscellaneous Methods of Print Production

The primary concern in the present study has been with machines which combine both a means for projecting the image of a microform so that it can be read and a means of producing an enlarged print of the image when desired.

Prior to the development of the reader-printers now on the market, the making of an enlarged print entailed sending the film to a photographic laboratory where the enlarged prints could be made. Should the film in question happen to be a 100-foot roll containing a thousand or more pages of unnumbered manuscript material, or a heterogeneous collection of short articles or excerpts from longer works, the problem of identifying the needed documents in a manner which would enable the photographer to locate and print them is no easy one. Between these two extremes, however, there now lies another solution which, in certain cases, and with admitted limitations, makes it possible for the research worker to make usable enlargements without sending the microform to a photographic laboratory and, at the same time, without the need on his part to acquire the knowledge and skills traditionally associated with the production of photographic enlargements.

This solution is based upon the use of high-speed stabilization process materials and a small processing unit such as the Polymicro.

The claims on the part of the manufacturers of stabilization processing units that such units replace the photographer and the darkroom are slightly exaggerated, but as they concern the practical needs of a research worker who needs rapidly produced prints from microforms, these claims come closer to being true. As was pointed out in the case of the Rollacopy, a stabilization processing unit has been combined with an enlarging device. Similar combining can be done with many other enlargers and also with external projection readers such as the Recordak Corporation's Model MPE reader and the Griscombe Products Corporation's portable microfilm reader, both of which handle 16 mm. and 35 mm. microfilm; the Huyghens and Super Dagmar readers, which handle microfiche; and the American Optical Company's Model 5075 reader for micro-opaques. (The last-named machine is no longer being manufactured.)

From the standpoint of convenience, one of the principal disadvantages encountered in combinations in which a stabilization processing unit is used in conjunction with a microform reader is that the light output of most readers is adjusted for an intensity which will be comfortable for reading, and which, at the same time, will be cool enough so that even though a frame of microfilm is exposed to the heat emitted by the projection lamp for relatively long periods of time, the film will not be damaged. Such a low level of illumination precludes the use of "room light" photographic papers unless long exposures are employed and the paper, which is in a face-up position, is shielded in some manner from the effects of ambient light. The alternative to this is to employ higher speed papers, but this necessitates the placement of the reader in an area in which ambient light can be reduced to a very low level when prints are to be made.

A second disadvantage in working with readers such as the Recordak MPE and the Griscombe portable stems from the fact that these readers work at fixed magnifications which are relatively high. These fixed magnifications are 19X for the Recordak MPE and 17X for the Griscombe portable. By raising the level of the surface on which the projected image falls, the magnification of the Griscombe portable reader can be reduced to approximately 12X. By using an accessory device known as the Fairfax Platen Elevator (Figures 58 and 59), manufactured by Fairfax Photo Products, Inc., Fort Lee, New Jersey, selling for $27.00, the magnification of the MPE

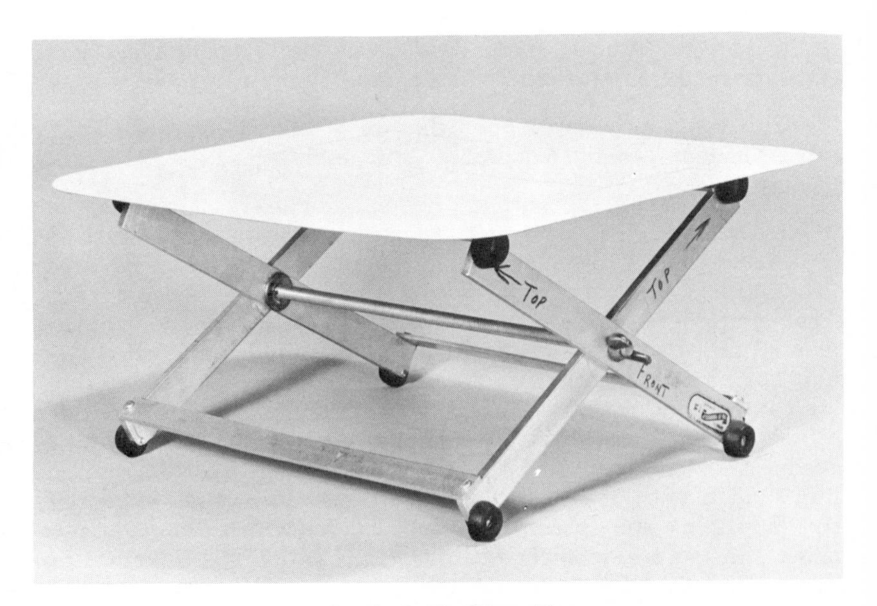

Fig. 58. The Fairfax Platen Elevator.

Fig. 59. Fairfax Platen Elevator in position in MPE reader.

can also be reduced to approximately 12X. A sheet of glass can be used to hold the sensitized paper flat.

To give examples of the relationship between paper speed, exposure, and the tolerance of certain papers to ambient light, a number of tests were made using the Recordak MPE reader with a test film having a background density of 1.6. The room lighting was arranged with a bare 150-watt lamp 6½ feet from the reader, but in a position where light did not shine directly on the hooded reader screen. The paper dispenser and the processor were five feet from the lamp. A sheet of Polyclair slow paper was taken from the paper dispenser in a face-down position and kept in this position until it was placed within the hood of the reader. It was then turned face up and the reader lamp turned on to make the exposure. The minimum exposure for an acceptable print was three minutes. At the end of the exposure interval, the paper was turned face down before removal from the reader and then processed. There was no evidence of fog under these conditions, and the 150-watt lamp provided ample illumination for the conduct of the printing and processing operations. A 3-minute exposure, however, might well be much too long if many prints were to be made. When the time to change frames and to place and process the sensitized paper is included, a 3-minute exposure yields prints at a production rate of about 16 per hour. Such a rate might still, however, have advantages to the user over sending the film to a photographic laboratory.

If faster papers are to be used in order to decrease the exposure time, ambient light must be diminished accordingly. For example, using Rollacopy M-5 paper, which is manufactured by Ets. Bauchet et Cie and distributed by the Andrews Paper and Chemical Company for use with Rollacopy printers, the exposure time was reduced to 9 seconds, but the conditions of ambient light used with the Polyclair paper were much too bright. Even with the 150-watt lamp at a distance of 10 feet from the work table and at an angle of 30 degrees to its surface, it was not possible to handle the paper in an upside-down position rapidly enough to eliminate fog. The fog, however, although causing an over-all grayish cast, did not interfere with the legibility of the image. Such a print, therefore, could be considered as successful if the intention was only to obtain a legible copy. Such conditions, however, oblige the user to work with rapidity and care. A preferable alternative would be to reduce the wattage of ambient light to a point where the danger of fog would be appreciably lessened, thus allowing a more comfortable time interval for the handling of the sensitized material.

Other readily available stabilization process papers, such as Polyclair Fast and Fotorite enlarging papers, are actually too fast to use in the manner described. In addition to their sensitivity to even very low levels of ambient light, the exposures from the test negative fell in a range of from 1½ to 2½ seconds which is much too short to be easily controllable. The use of these papers, however, has one distinct advantage, and that is that they can be obtained in degrees of contrast which are much lower than the relatively high degree of contrast normally found in photocopy papers, regardless of the process. If, as is often the case, the center of the field of illumination of a microfilm reader is brighter than the corners, this difference in brightness becomes exaggerated on prints made on high-contrast papers. The center of the print may be overexposed to the point of illegibility while the corners are still too underexposed and faint to read. By using materials which have low contrast, the effects of uneven illumination can be minimized, thus allowing both the center and the corners of the image to reproduce legibly. Prints made on low-contrast materials are usually quite satisfactory since micro-images generally tend to be quite high in contrast.

A paper which combines moderate contrast with a speed permitting exposures to be easily controlled is Fotorite RK 41. This paper is supplied in four degrees of contrast ranging from low to high. Exposures of the test negative in the MPE reader using contrast grade No. 1 were about 10 seconds. The cost, however, of continuous-tone papers is much greater than photocopy papers. Eight and one-half by 11-inch sheets of Fotorite RK 41 paper in lots of 100 cost almost 13 cents each.

Low-contrast papers also offer to the user a material which is much better suited to the reproduction of continuous-tone illustrations. In most negative microfilms, the tone scale of continuous-tone illustrations has been greatly exaggerated by the high contrast of the material itself and the development it receives. When such illustrations are, in turn, reproduced on a high contrast photocopy paper, the results are barely recognizable and contain nothing of the detail dependent upon tonal gradations which the original illustration possesses. But when negatives of continuous-tone illustrations are reproduced on low contrast materials, much more of the tonal scale appears on the print. This is not to say that the prints are accurate reproductions of the original illustration. To exaggerate the tone scale by using a negative material of high contrast, and then to cut the contrast back by printing the negative on a low contrast paper is far from the ideal means of making a good copy of an illustration possessing a long tone scale. But, nevertheless, prints made on low contrast papers are infinitely superior to prints made on the usual run of photocopy papers which are ordinarily used for enlargements from microfilms.

The pressing need on the part of many research workers to have some means whereby an enlarged print from a micro-opaque might be made has prompted the investigation of a combination of a micro-opaque reader with high speed stabilization printing and processing. The reader which appeared to be the most promising one for this purpose was the American Optical Company's Model 5075 (Figure 60). This reader is capable of handling all sizes of micro-opaques and projects an image to a plane surface on which a sheet of sensitized material can be placed. After preliminary tests were made to determine what types of sensitized materials might be best suited to the light output of the reader, a series of tests were conducted with Fotorite RK 41 paper, contrast grade No. 1. In these tests a number of prints were made from several specimens of each of the three major micro-opaque forms — Microcards, Microlex, and Microprint. It was found that in printing from Microcards with the 20X lens, exposures in a range of from 15 to 20 seconds were satisfactory. The definition of the screen image, however, and hence of the print, was only adequately legible if the text of the original was fairly large and clear. In printing from a number of Microcards of important scientific serials, subscript and superscript numbers, mathematical formulae, and footnotes were neither clear on the reader screen nor on the print. Microlex im-

Fig. 60. The American Optical Company Model 5075 micro-opaque reader.

ages fared a little better because law reports do not ordinarily include type sizes, line widths, or finely detailed drawings such as are common in scientific works. Microprint images reproduced the best of the three since Microprint images are produced lithographically instead of photographically and hence exhibit much more sharply defined line images.

These tests pointed up a number of significant factors relating to the problems involved in making enlarged prints from micro-opaques. In the first place, micro-opaque images which are produced photographically by contact printing on silver halide materials exhibit a decided loss of definition which adversely affects legibility. Expressed in another and perhaps more meaningful way, the reduction ratios used in filming for the purpose of compressing the maximum amount of material in a minimum amount of card space are too great for many of the subjects. The result of this is that the screened images of finely detailed subjects are simply not legible, much less printable in legible form.

Prints from Microlex cards were superior in legibility to prints from many Microcards, but this was simply because the type size of Microlex subjects is larger than the type size encountered in many of the subjects which have been reproduced on Microcards. With Microlex, the size of the type used in the publishing of the originals permits the use of high reduction ratios without serious loss of legibility. With Microcards, the reduction ratio appears to be much more arbitrary. Page size and the economic factor of the number of pages per card appear to be the prime determinants of the reduction ratio employed, without proper regard for size of type or fineness of detail.

While the focusing system employed in the American Optical Company's reader leaves something to be desired, the optical performance of the instrument was quite satisfactory. The projection of a number of test objects showed that the lenses were very good indeed.

On the basis of the results of the tests conducted, it is clear that the primary problem which any designer of a reader-printer for micro-opaques faces is the lack of sharpness of photographically produced micro-opaques, especially Microcards. If the micro-opaque image itself is not sharp, no expensive optical system nor refinement in printing can ever produce a legible copy.

13 Summary of Findings

As the previous chapters have shown, the situation with respect to reader-printers for library use is, by and large, a disappointing one. Most of the machines tested fail to qualify for library use for reasons which can now be summarized.

The processes

There are two processes employed in the reader-printers tested which reproduce from microtransparencies: the electrolytic process employed in the Filmac line of reader-printers and the stabilization process employed in all of the others. The electrolytic process yields prints which are: (a) low in contrast and often unsatisfactory if a positive microfilm is being reproduced; (b) heavy in weight, with a strong tendency to curl or sag when filed vertically;* (c) remarkable in their exposure latitude; and (d) presumably stable. Prints produced by the stabilization process are: (a) relatively high in contrast; (b) also tend to curl, since they are coated on one side (but are much lighter in weight than electrolytically produced prints; (c) limited in their exposure latitude; and (d) of dubious stability. Either process produces a finished print in a matter of seconds, but electrolytically produced prints are much less moist. Both processes are "negative-positive" processes yielding a positive print from a negative transparency.

The types of reader-printers

Of the two types of reader-printers — the "internal projection" type and the "external projection" type — internal projection reader-printers offer the very great advantage of easy and convenient use under strong conditions of ambient light. External projection reader-printers offer the user a choice between long exposures under room-light conditions or short exposures if virtual darkroom conditions are established. Unfortunately, none of the internal projection reader-printers (with the exception of the

*The Minnesota Mining and Manufacturing Company has recently brought out a new paper for use with the Filmac 200 which is not only much lighter in weight but which was designed to eliminate a potential hazard present in the heavier paper, which, because of its electro-conductive properties, could be dangerous if used near open electrical circuits.

Filmac 300) comes anywhere near being capable of producing full-size or nearly full-size prints from the variety of microtransparencies found in libraries with anything approaching efficiency and economy.

In the external projection reader-printers tested — the Universel and the Rollacopy (alias Micromate) — what is offered as a reader-printer is a microfilm projecting device to which has been added an easel for holding a sheet of sensitized paper and an exposure timing device. The microfilm projector has thus been converted into a kind of photographic enlarger. With each of the machines, a stabilization processing device has been added so that the exposed prints can be quickly processed on the spot without the need for the space and usual paraphernalia of a photographic darkroom. Such an assemblage of components, however, does not make a reader-*printer* but something which might better be called a reader-*enlarger*. The distinction being drawn here has to do with the degree of automation, not only in terms of the relative amounts of work being performed by the machine and by the operator, but also in terms of the requisite knowledge and skills demanded of the operator if rapid, efficient, and economic use is to be made of either machine.

One of the serious difficulties encountered in using internal projection reader-printers, such as the Filmac 100 and the Documat, for the reproduction of library microforms is in the control of the image size; it must be remembered, however, that these machines were not designed with library microforms in mind. When these machines are used for the purpose for which they were intended — the reading and printing of the office-record class of documents — control of image size is much less of a problem. Assuming, then, that either machine is being used for its intended purpose, the basic steps required of the operator are those of: (a) locating the desired frame, (b) focusing the image, (c) setting the exposure control, and (d) pressing a button. With external projection reader-printers such as the Universel or the Rollacopy, the operator also must locate the desired frame, but, unlike the Filmac 100 and Documat, this operation requires the use of both hands instead of only one.

Following this, the image must be focused and the exposure control set. But, at this point, no mere pushing of a button does the rest. Instead, the operator must: (a) open the easel, (b) obtain a sheet of sensitized paper from an envelope or dispenser (keeping it shielded as much as possible from ambient light), (c) carefully position the paper on the easel, (d) close the easel, (e) press the exposure button, (f) open the easel, (g) remove the sensitized sheet, (h) close the easel, (i) insert the exposed sheet into the processor, and (j) remove it. With the Rollacopy, the additional step of closing down the lens aperture to a smaller opening for optimum sharpness may be required, and with the Universel, the mirror may have to be aligned.

Another point of comparison, which has to do with the knowledge required of the operator, occurs in connection with changes in magnification. While fixed magnifications in internal projection reader-printers have certain drawbacks, changing the magnification by changing lenses does not require a change in exposure since both the relative aperture of the different lenses and the lamp-to-screen distance remain the same. Changing the magnification on an external projection reader-printer, however, does require a change in exposure. Other things being equal, the lower the magnification ratio, and hence the shorter the lamp-to-easel distance, the shorter the exposure will be. As the magnification is increased, the exposure required will be progressively longer in accordance with the law of inverse squares. Thus, along with the ordinary problems of exposure determination with which an operator must cope, an additional variable is introduced whenever the magnification is changed. Because, in dealing with library microforms, an operator may frequently encounter a variety of sizes, formats, and reduction ratios which will require changes in magnification, accurate exposure determinations will depend on how much experience and skill the operator has accrued in the use of the machine.

Reader-printers as readers

In considering only the reader function of reader-printers in relation to library microforms, the reader-printers tested exhibited a number of shortcomings which stem primarily from the fact that for the most part they were not designed with library microforms in mind. Readers *or* reader-printers which have been designed for viewing or printing office-type records are usually much too limited in screen size and magnification control to be useful as readers for library microforms. This is particularly true of such devices as the Filmac 100 and the Documat.

The Filmac 200-R, which at least has a screen size large enough for viewing 35 mm. microcopies of newspapers, fails as a reader for such microcopies through lack of adequate coverage of the full 35-mm. frame commonly used in two-page-per-frame newspaper filming, and through lack of an image rotation control for viewing newspapers filmed in a one-page-per-frame position.

The Universel and the Micromate began as microfilm readers to which additional components have been added to make them into reader-printers, but even as readers their capabilities are limited.

The Ross Microreader suffers as a reader from the attempt to provide a machine which would handle all common library microforms. In general, its performance with any of the microforms which it will accept is not as good as that of other readers designed for the reading of one particular microform.

The Microcard Copier cannot be considered a reader at all, since the image which is viewed for positioning the desired page for printing is much too small for convenient reading.

The one reader-printer which does function fairly well as a reader for library microforms is the Filmac 300, since it does provide a fairly large screen image, image rotation control, and a continuous range of magnifications. But, considered only as a reader, the price of $3,600 is exceedingly high.

In general, it can be said of the reader-printers investigated in the course of this study that their utility to the library world as readers or as reader-printers is limited by the size and format of the microforms for which they were specifically designed or by the fact that their capabilities as readers have been subordinated to their function as printers.

The librarian who might contemplate the attractive possibility of "killing two birds with one stone" by acquiring a needed reader which he can also use as a reader-printer must recognize that the choice of such a machine from equipment available at this time will provide him with a reader which will be much less satisfactory than numerous other readers far better suited for viewing library microforms and will cost him a far greater capital outlay.

Reader-printers excluded from the testing program

For reasons similar to those given above, a number of reader-printers, some of which are widely advertised, were not considered to be eligible candidates in a testing program the purpose of which was to evaluate equipment suitable for the reproduction of library microforms. There were two bases for exclusion: (1) Reader-printers that were simply larger-size models of equipment which was tested but which did not differ fundamentally in other respects; and (2) reader-printers that were known to have design limitations of one or more kinds which would significantly hamper their utility in reproducing from library microforms.

Reader-printers which were not tested for the first reason given include the following three, all of which are manufactured by the Federal Manufacturing and Engineering Company of Garden City, New York, and equipped with Polymicro stabilization processing units imported from France.

1. *The Rollacopier "17."* This machine is essentially nothing more than a larger version of the Rollacopy which was tested. A larger base equipped with a paper drawer, a larger paper easel,

a taller column, and a wider processing unit are provided in order to make prints up to 17 by 22 inches. The same type of projector is used but it is mounted in a horizontal position and equipped with a mirror at a 45-degree angle in front of the lens which projects the image downward to the paper easel. The Rollacopier "17" is priced at $595.

2. *The Micromate Model 24.* This machine differs from the smaller model Micromate (or Rollacopy) which was tested only in that the baseboard, paper easel, and processing unit are larger, the column is taller and is braced on both sides for greater rigidity, and a different exposure timing device is used. Like the smaller model, the projector is in a vertical position for direct downward projection. The Micromate Model 24 makes prints up to 18 by 24 inches and is priced at $745 or $785, depending upon the type of lens supplied.

3. *The Model 1820 Elliott Micro-3.* The Model 1820 Elliott Micro-3 is simply the Micromate Model 24 under the trade name given to it by the B. K. Elliott Company which distributes it. It is priced by this company at $765.

Reader-printers which were not tested for the second reason given include four which employ electrostatic processes for print production and three employing the stabilization process.

1. *The Xerox 1824 printer.* As the name implies, the Xerox 1824 printer employs the xerographic electrostatic process to produce prints up to 18 by 24 inches from microtransparencies. There are two models of the Xerox 1824 printer, one of which was designed to reproduce microtransparencies of engineering drawings mounted in EAM cards and which is known as the *"aperture card input model."* The second model is known as the *"universal input model"* since, in addition to microtransparencies mounted in EAM cards, it will also accept jacketed or sheet microfilm up to 5 by 8 inches and is also equipped with an accessory roll holder for printing from 16 mm. or 35 mm. microfilm in roll form. As with other machines which employ the xerographic process, permanent prints are produced very rapidly (21-30 seconds) on a plain, uncoated paper stock, and the process is completely dry. The disadvantages, however, from the standpoint of library use are the following:

a. The Xerox 1824 printer is not a *reader*-printer since the screen on which the projected image of a microtransparency appears is only about 4 by 4½ inches and is thus much too small for comfortable reading. The screen is essentially a viewing screen for the positioning of the microtransparency for printing and for the determination of the size of the print paper needed.

b. The magnification ratio is fixed at 14.5:1. As was brought out in the analysis of several of the reader-printers tested, lack of control over the magnification ratio can be a decided disadvantage in printing from microtransparencies of library materials since the reduction ratios used in filming are frequently much lower or much higher than 14.5:1.

c. Since this machine, like the Filmac 200-R, was designed primarily for the making of prints from 35 mm. microfilms of engineering drawings, the aperture in the optical system is not large enough to permit the projection of the full length of the modified 35 mm. frame which is widely used in the microfilming of newspapers and other large-size originals. Furthermore, reduction ratios substantially higher than 14.5:1 are often used in newspaper filming. If, for example, a newspaper file is filmed at a reduction ratio of 18 or 19 diameters and is then printed at a magnification ratio of only 14.5 diameters, this reduction in size may make the text rather difficult to read. Such a reduction in size would be particularly troublesome in prints from microfilms of nineteenth century newspapers in which the use of very small type faces was a common practice. In modern newspapers, the legibility of finely printed subject matter such as stock exchange reports would also be impaired by such a reduction from original size.

d. Low unit costs per print are only possible if the monthly volume of printing is quite high. The minimum rental cost per month for the universal input model is $205. This rental charge covers the cost of the first 2,000 prints made each month. An additional charge of 2 cents is made for all prints in excess of 2,000 per month. The universal input model may also be purchased outright for $18,500.

From the standpoint of library use, therefore, the limitations of the machine, together with the high cost of rental or purchase, make it of doubtful interest. Should a library happen to possess quantities of microtransparencies which had been filmed at reduction ratios compatible with the magnification ratio of the Xerox 1824 printer, and should there be sufficient demand for enlarged prints from such microtransparencies to defray the fixed monthly rental cost, the Xerox 1824 printer would be a likely choice, but such a situation would be a highly unusual one. Another situation in which the Xerox 1824 printer might be used to good advantage would be one in which a collection or collections of important research materials which had not hitherto been filmed were filmed to specifications which would meet the capabilities of the Xerox 1824 printer, again assuming that the demand for enlarged prints would be fairly high. A development somewhat along these lines is now under way in connection with the publication of the technical reports of the National Aeronautics and Space Administration on 5- by 8-inch sheet microfilm. Since the universal input model of the Xerox 1824 printer will accept a 5- by 8-inch sheet, the Information Dynamics

Corporation, which is engaged in producing the microtransparencies of the NASA reports, is filming them at a reduction ratio of 15.5:1. This reduction ratio permits the printing of three pages at a time on a 24-inch-long sheet and at only a slight reduction from original size.

2. *The Bruning Copytron, Model 1000.* The Bruning Copytron employs the Electrofax electrostatic process developed by the Radio Corporation of America. In this process, the paper used has a zinc oxide coating which is capable of holding an electrostatic charge. In other respects, the process is quite similar to xerography in that the image is made up of a finely divided powder which clings to the coated surface of the paper by means of electrostatic attraction and is subsequently fused to the paper by heat to form a permanent image. Like the Xerox 1824 printer, the Copytron was designed primarily for the reproduction of engineering drawings and is also available in two models — one for microtransparencies mounted in EAM cards and another which will also accept microfilm in roll form. Also like the Xerox 1824, the Copytron has only a 5- by 8-inch viewing screen for positioning microtransparencies for printing instead of a full-size reading screen. The machine can be set to make prints of any of 6 different sizes between a minimum of 8½ by 11 inches and a maximum of 18 by 24 inches. Finished prints are produced in 30 seconds or less.

Unlike the Xerox 1824, some control of magnification is possible with the Copytron. The basic model provides limited magnification control within a range of from 14 to 16 diameters, but auxiliary heads which provide magnification ratios of 8:1, 12:1, and 20:1 are available. Depending upon the magnification ratio selected, the price of the Copytron ranges from $9,750 to $10,000. Additional auxiliary heads for different magnification ratios are priced at $1,500 each. A lease-to-purchase plan is also available, whereby the purchase price of the machine can be contracted over a 36-month period. The supplies needed for making prints in an 8½- by 11-inch size (paper and toner) cost approximately 3½ cents per print. The cost of making larger prints is proportionally greater, according to size.

While the Copytron does offer a greater degree of control over magnification than a number of similar machines, only a few fixed magnifications are available. This, plus the limitation of a small viewing screen and a very high list price or costly monthly lease payments combine to make the Copytron of doubtful interest to libraries.

3. *Polydex reader-printers.* There are two models of the Polydex reader-printer — one which handles 16 mm. roll film (Model M16) and one which handles 35 mm. microfilms (Model M35) in EAM cards. Prints are produced in approximately 25 sec-

onds by means of the Electrofax electrostatic process. The 35 mm. model produces prints in sizes ranging from 8½ by 11 inches to 18 by 24 inches at a materials cost of 20 cents for the largest size. The magnification ratio of the lens is in a narrow range of from 14.5:1 to 15:1. A model which will accept 35 mm. film in roll form will not be available until April, 1963. The list price for the roll-film model has been given at $1,995.

Like the Xerox 1824 printer and the Copytron Model 1000, the Polydex Model M35 has been primarily designed for the reproduction of microtransparencies of engineering drawings and the magnification ratio of the lens has been selected to meet engineering drawing reproduction requirements. Such limitations alone would make the roll-film model of doubtful utility as a reader-printer for library microforms.

4. *The Ricohfax.* The Ricohfax is a small reader-printer of Japanese manufacture which employs the Electrofax electrostatic process for print production. It is far more limited in its capabilities than any of the three previous machines described in that it was designed primarily for the reproduction of small engineering drawings (9 by 12 inches) and operates at the extremely low fixed magnification of 6.75:1. Because of such limitations, it cannot be considered to be useful for printing from library microforms.

5. *The Photostat 18-24 reader-printer.* Like the Polydex, the Filmac 200-R, and others, the Photostat 18-24 reader-printer was designed primarily for the making of enlarged prints from microtransparencies of engineering drawings. Prints are produced by means of the two-bath stabilization process. Again, two models are available — one for microtransparencies in EAM cards and one which will accept microfilm in roll form. In keeping with engineering drawing reproduction requirements, the magnification is fixed at 14.7:1, but lenses of other magnifications may be obtained on special order. A masking device is provided which enables the user to print any portion of the projected image between a minimum paper length of 8 inches and a maximum length of 24 inches. The width of prints is controlled by loading the machine with roll stock paper in widths ranging from 11 to 18 inches. Thus, with 11-inch-wide roll stock, the smallest print that can be made would be 8 by 11 inches and the largest print on roll stock 18 inches wide would measure 18 by 24 inches. Prints are cut to any pre-set length before they are delivered from the machine and are produced in approximately 30 seconds at a materials cost of 8 cents per square foot.

The roll-film model is priced at $3,130 or can be rented for $100 per month.

As a reader-printer for library microforms, the drawbacks of the Photostat 18-24 are similar to those of the Filmac 200-R. While the Photostat 18-24 is also a true reader, in that it is equipped with an 18- by 24-inch screen, there is no provision for rotating the image. Thus all library microforms which are filmed with the lines of text parallel to the short axis of the film (such as newspapers filmed in position 1-A, Figure 14) would appear on the reader screen with the lines of text in a vertical rather than a horizontal position. Also, as with other reader-printers designed for engineering drawing requirements, the optical system is not capable of projecting the full length of the modified frame commonly used in the filming of newspapers. The masking device makes it possible to print one page — i.e., half of a frame — of newspapers filmed in position 2-B (Figure 14) without wastage of materials, but the magnification ratio is substantially lower than the reduction ratios commonly used for two-page-per-frame newspaper filming. Legibility will therefore be affected by this unavoidable reduction in size.

6. *Recordak Lodestar reader-printers.* The Recordak Lodestar reader-printers are rather costly and highly specialized devices for the reading and printing of 16 mm. microfilms only. The simplest model, the PSV, has an exposure unit which accepts cut sheets of paper, and a separate, hand-fed stabilization processor. Reconditioned units only are available at a cost of $1,020 or at a rental of $50.00 per month with a minimum rental charge of $300. The Model PES has an automated processing unit within the body of the machine and sells for $2,650 or can be rented for $72.00 per month with a minimum rental charge of $432. Both models can be obtained with an accessory device called an "Image Control Keyboard" which makes possible very rapid location of any given frame on a roll, but only films which have been specially prepared for use with the Image Control Keyboard can be used with this device. Since neither device has any provision for image rotation, documents which are to be read on Lodestar equipment must be filmed in one position only. The Model PSV, with Image Control Keyboard, sells for $4,600 or can be rented for $150 per month with a minimum rental charge of $900. The Model PES, with Image Control Keyboard, sells for $5,895 or can be rented for $170 per month with a minimum rental charge of $1,020.

7. *The Filmarcor.* The Filmarcor is a reader-printer of French manufacture which has never been imported, although it has been nationally advertised in trade publications in this country. The distributing firm which had originally made arrangements with the manufacturer for United States distribution rights reported that it had recommended to the manufacturer that certain design changes be made in the machine before attempts were made to market it in this country.

Design and Construction

As the chapters devoted to the machines show, most of the

machines exhibit design or construction faults, some of which are relatively minor and might easily have been remedied by the manufacturer, and others which are major and not easy to remedy. One design fault in particular, encountered in several machines, is worth singling out for discussion.

When one considers the relative complexity of the better, more highly automated reader-printers, the high degree of engineering skill required to ensure excellent optical, chemical, and mechanical performance, the efficient manufacturing techniques and controls which must be established for the production of a uniform and consistently functioning product, and the relatively high list prices commanded by such products, one could reasonably expect that such a simple but important thing in an optical device as the method by which the image is focused would be fully considered by the designer with a view toward maximum efficiency, ease of use, and accuracy. It was surprising, therefore, to find in several of the reader-printers tested that the mechanical means by which the image was to be brought into focus was actually quite crude.

Ideally, the focusing mechanism should be such that by a turn of a knob the image can be brought smoothly from an out-of-focus position to an in-focus position and on to another out-of-focus position. In other words, the focusing knob should move the lens from a position which is too far from the film plane to form a sharp image to another position which is too near to the film plane, with the correct point of focus lying between these two extremes. The change between these two extremes should be neither too slow nor too abrupt to be easily perceived. To the human eye, the appearance of image sharpness or definition is a relative thing, and the focusing of an image thus becomes a process of "zeroing in," whereby one goes back and forth between successively closer points on either side of the ideal focus until optimum sharpness and clarity are achieved. If the device controlling the movement of the lens moves it too much or too quickly in either direction, proper focus becomes acutely critical and difficult of achievement. The slightest movement of the hand on the focusing control may be too much. If, on the other hand, the movement of the lens is too slow, changes in the relative sharpness of the image become imperceptible until the image becomes seriously out of focus. The relativity of the "zeroing in" process thus becomes lost through the slowness with which any perceptible change in sharpness occurs.

Of the various focusing mechanisms encountered in the reader-printers tested, the method commonly used in hand cameras — in which the lens is mounted in a barrel and moves in and out by means of a helical thread — proved to be the most satisfactory. The efficiency of the helical thread method depends, however, on the pitch of the threads. In the Filmac line of reader-printers, the pitch of the thread is such that the image moves easily and smoothly in and out of focus with a single turn of the hand. But in the Universel, the pitch of the thread is so shallow that one must turn the lens many times to produce any perceptible change in the appearance of the image.

The Rollacopy employs a helical mount which is somewhat different in design. While the pitch of the thread is satisfactory, the mounting of the lens and the lens barrel permits too much play which causes lateral movement of the image as it is being focused. This shifting of the position of the image on the easel, which occurs every time the lens is rotated for focusing, is disturbing to the eye and makes focusing unnecessarily difficult. In addition to this, the lack of rigidity of the column causes still another kind of movement of the projected image. If, for example, the projector is raised on the column to a magnification of 10 diameters, the weight of the projector when it is this high on the column causes the entire assembly to be shaky. Unless the greatest care is used in rotating the lens for focusing, some movement of the projector, and hence of the projected image, occurs. The projector may move only $\frac{1}{32}$ inch but, because of the magnification, the movement of the projected image is ten times as great, or $\frac{10}{32}$ inch. Thus, at higher magnifications, it becomes especially difficult to focus a finely detailed image to the point of maximum sharpness.

In the Documat, which uses a screw thread device to force the lens closer to the film plane and a coil spring to force the lens further away, the screw thread moves the lens smoothly and positively. The coil spring arrangement, however, does not work so smoothly. Play and/or friction between the lens barrel and its enclosing cylinder causes the outward movement to be jerky and abrupt. But even at best the screw thread arrangement on the Documat is too slow in its action. Too many turns of the focusing knob are necessary to bring the image into optimum focus.

The problems of producing a successful reader-printer are unquestionably manifold; but for the manufacturers of such devices to fail in engineering a simple, smooth-working, positive focusing mechanism only adds, and quite unnecessarily, to the problems that an operator will encounter in attempting to make successful, high quality reproductions on such machines. From the user's standpoint, ease of focusing is sufficiently important that the focusing mechanism is one of the last places where a manufacturer should permit careless engineering, or stint for economy at the expense of efficiency. One might expect to find in, say, a "dime store" toy microscope selling for $9.95 a focusing mechanism in which the movement is too slow or too abrupt, jerky, shaky, or uneven, but in machines costing upward of 100 times as much, the consumer might reasonably expect something better.

Costs

No cost tables have been attempted with each of the reader-printers tested simply because the number of variables which can affect the cost per print is very great indeed.

Of the two processes which currently dominate the picture, the electrolytic process used in the Filmac line of reader-printers provides considerable exposure latitude whereas the stabilization process is rather limited in this respect. More trial-and-error exposures will be required with the latter than with the former, and waste will therefore be higher. How much waste may be involved will depend primarily upon the knowledge and skill of the operator. In the hands of an unskilled operator, the waste factor with machines such as the Rollacopy or Universel can be very high.

Correct exposure is dependent upon a number of factors, such as the contrast of the film being reproduced, the contrast of the sensitized material used, the background density of the negative or line density of the positive, the sharpness of the microform image, the sharpness of the reproducing lens, the size of the characters (line and space widths) of the projected image, the speed of the sensitized material, the degree of enlargement, and so forth.

The wide exposure latitude of the electrolytic process provides the operator with a margin of error which frees him from having to pay more than minimal attention to these factors, but with the stabilization process, particularly with external projection reader-printers, the margin of error is much smaller and far more knowledge and experience are required of the operator if remakes due to incorrect exposures are to be avoided.

Another variable affecting costs has to do with the distribution of the needed frames within a roll of film. Will ten prints be made from 10 successive frames of a single article, in which the reduction ratio, degree of magnification, and background density will be uniform, and thus printable at a consistent, repetitive exposure, or will the ten prints be made from 10 frames randomly located within a 100-foot roll of film, and with the further possibility that each frame may have a different background density and require a different degree of magnification?

Costs, therefore, are dependent on many variable and subjective factors and are in no way predictable. The only fixed figures which can be given are those of the materials themselves.

Printing from micro-opaques

The present situation with respect to equipment for making enlarged prints from micro-opaque images is even more disappointing than is the case with reader-printers for microtransparencies, and this for two reasons in particular. In the first place, both of

TABLE 6

ELECTROLYTIC PROCESS MATERIALS

(Manufacturer: Minnesota Mining and Manufacturing Company)

Machine	Size of Roll Stock	Size of Print	Number of Prints per Roll	Cost per Roll (in Lots of Four Rolls)	Cost per Print	Cost of Chemicals per Pint	Approximate Cost of Chemicals per Print*
Filmac 100	8½″ x 298′	8½″ x 11″	300	$25.71	$ .085	$1.25	⅓¢
Filmac 300	8½″ x 300′	8½″ x 11″†	300	25.92	.085	1.25	⅓¢
Filmac 300	11″ x 300′	11″ x 14″†	250	33.53	.135	1.25	½¢
Filmac 200 and 200-R	18″ x 237′	18″ x 26″	108	28.06	.26	1.25	1¼¢

*Chemical costs will be higher if machine use is intermittent and evaporation of the solution occurs.

†Maximum print sizes are given. Smaller prints can be made on the Filmac 300.

TABLE 7

ROLL-STOCK STABILIZATION PROCESS MATERIALS

Machine	Size of Roll Stock	Size of Print	Number of Prints per Roll	Cost per Roll (in Lots of Two Rolls)	Cost per Print	Cost of Chemicals per Quart	Approximate Cost of Chemicals per Print*
Documat MKI	8½″ x 150′	8½″ x 11″	160	$12.50	$ .078	$1.35	¾¢
Documat MKII (Monobath)	8½″ x 150′	8½″ x 11″	160	12.50	.078	1.70	1¢
Documat MKII (Two-Solution)	8½″ x 150′	8½″ x 11″	160	12.00	.075	1.15† 2.25‡	1¢

*Chemical costs will be higher if machine use is intermittent and evaporation of the solution occurs.

†Developer.

‡Stabilizer.

TABLE 8

CUT-SHEET STABILIZATION PROCESS MATERIALS

Trade Name of Materials	Manufacturer	Type	Cost per 8½- by 11-Inch Print (in Lots of 100)	Cost of Chemicals per Quart	Approximate Cost of Chemicals per Print*
Polyclair	Polyclair (France)	Photocopy, slow	$ .0695	Developer: $1.65 Stabilizer: 2.50	⅔¢
Polyclair	Polyclair (France)	Glossy,† Continuous-tone, Rapid	.11	Developer: 1.65 Stabilizer: 2.50	⅔¢
Rollacopy	Ets. Bauchet et Cie (France)	Photocopy (M-5)	.05	Developer: 1.25 Stabilizer: 2.50	⅔¢
Fotorite	Mimosa (West Germany)	Photocopy	.0915	Developer: 1.95 Stabilizer: 2.50	⅔¢
Fotorite	Mimosa (West Germany)	Glossy,‡ Continuous-tone, Rapid (RB-11)	.1265	Developer: 1.95 Stabilizer: 2.50	⅔¢
Fotorite	Mimosa (West Germany)	Glossy, Continuous-tone, Slow (RK-41)	.1265	Developer: 1.95 Stabilizer: 2.50	⅔¢
Royal Scot	Hunter Photo Copyist, Inc. (United States)	Photocopy, Slow	.0559	Developer: 1.40 Stabilizer: 2.48	⅔¢
Royal Scot	Hunter Photo Copyist, Inc. (United States)	Photocopy, Rapid	.0625	Developer: 1.40 Stabilizer: 2.48	⅔¢

*Chemical costs will be higher if machine use is intermittent and evaporation of the solution occurs.

†Available in contrast grades No. 1, No. 2, and No. 3.

‡Available in contrast grades No. 1, No. 2, No. 3, and No. 4.

TABLE 9

ROLL STOCK DIFFUSION-TRANSFER-

REVERSAL MATERIALS

Machine	Size of Roll Stock	Size of Print	Number of Prints per Roll
Microcard Copier Type I	8½″ x 98′	8½″ x 13″	90

Machine	Cost per Set of Two Rolls (1 neg. + 1 pos.)	Cost per Print	Cost of Chemicals per Quart	Approximate Cost of Chemicals per Print*
Microcard Copier Type I	$10.76	$ .12	$1.15	⅔¢

*Chemical costs will be higher if machine use is intermittent and evaporation and/or aerial oxidation of the solution occurs.

the reader-printers tested which are at all capable of printing from micro-opaques — the Ross Microreader and the Microcard Copier — failed, for the reasons which have been given, to turn in satisfactory performances. In the second place, the need for a device for making enlarged prints from micro-opaques is in many ways even more pressing than the need for a microtransparency reader-printer.

The first true reader-printer for microtransparencies worthy of the name was the Filmac 100, introduced in 1958. But, prior to this time, hundreds of millions of enlarged copies from microtransparencies had been produced by a variety of means, ranging from prints of single frames made by ordinary enlarging methods in a photographic darkroom to the rapid and automatic enlargement of entire 100-foot rolls of film such as was done during World War II in the "V-mail" and "Airgraph" systems and later by Xerox "Copyflo." Individual or quantity printing from microtransparencies has always been possible since microtransparencies are simply a class of photographic negatives which can be reproduced by the usual methods of photographic enlarging. A micro-opaque image, on the other hand, is not reproducible in enlarged form by conventional photographic printing techniques.

A glance at the catalogs of publications available in the form of micro-opaques shows at once what a vast body of literature has by now been published or reprinted in micro-opaque form. Much of this material is out of print and, in many instances is now so scarce that it almost never appears on the second-hand book market. Libraries in need of such materials can now obtain them in micro-opaque form, and although micro-opaques are by no means equivalent to original volumes in terms of ease and convenience of use, or to microtransparencies in terms of image quality, nevertheless, as one librarian put it, "A microcopy in the hand is worth a whole flock of originals in the bibliographic bush." Today, however, the possession of a microcopy of a given work is not enough.

Only a few years ago, if a research worker in California could obtain a photostat of a scientific article from a library in New York, this was still something of a luxury and not an inexpensive one at that. Since then, however, the appearance on the market of a great many new, simple, rapid, and relatively inexpensive photocopying processes and machines has changed the picture considerably. The research worker of today has become more and more accustomed to having his own photocopies of research materials even if the original is in a library in the same building! More and more, the trend is for photocopies to come to the scholar, instead of vice versa, even if the distance is only a hundred yards. This in itself tends to alter and expedite the manner in which research work is done; the research worker is no longer bound by the restrictions of library hours and "library use only" circulation restrictions.

Ironically, if a library has substantially increased its resources by taking advantage of the technological advance achieved through the development of micro-opaques, the research worker is aided by the fact that the information he seeks is available. At the same time, he is decidedly hampered in his freedom to make use of the material expeditiously and conveniently. If the material was in the form of a bound volume he might obtain a photocopy or at least might be able to take the volume to his office where he could peruse it at his leisure. But if the material is in micro-opaque form, he can neither obtain a photocopy nor can he use the material at a time and place of his own choosing unless he is fortunate enough to have several hundred dollars to spend on a reading device. Because it is usually the library which provides the reading equipment for micro-opaques, the scholar of the mid-twentieth century is as effectively bound by the location of material in micro-opaque form as the medieval scholar was by chain-bindings! This kind of bottleneck in the business of research surely needs to be broken. The obstacles standing in the way of the development of a successful reader-printer which will produce enlarged copies from micro-opaques appear to be partly economic and partly technological. The economic fact is that a high-precision, highly automated optical printing device for micro-opaques cannot be engineered and then manufactured in relatively small quantities except at quite a high price. The technological problem lies in the fact that micro-opaque images, size for size, are by no means as sharp and well defined as microtransparencies. In many micro-opaques which were examined, small type faces and fine details are often just barely legible. Even with an optical printing device of the very highest quality, it is questionable whether such fine details would be legible on an enlarged print.

Recommendations

A successful reader-printer for microtransparencies of library materials should include some of the features found in reader-printers now on the market and many features which are not. The following recommendations are therefore offered:

Type. As was brought out in the analyses of the machines tested, internal projection reader-printers are preferable to external projection models simply because of the advantage of being able to use them under conditions of ordinary room light. Furthermore, the internal projection principle carries with it the concomitant advantage of a much greater degree of automation than is exhibited by external projection devices. Conceivably a much more highly automated external projection reader-printer could be designed and built, but there is nothing even remotely like this on the market today.

Process. No firm recommendation can be made as to which process might be best in terms of the needs of the librarian or the scholar. Each of the various processes which might be successfully employed in a reader-printer has advantages and disadvantages. The xerographic process is dry, and the prints are permanent, but machine costs tend to be very high. The diffusion-transfer-reversal process is a positive-to-positive process which may be advantageous in printing from positive microtransparencies or micro-opaques, but this advantage is lost in printing from negative microtransparencies. The electrolytic process is a negative-to-positive process, low in contrast but which possesses great exposure latitude. Its performance in printing from positive microtransparencies, however, is not satisfactory in all cases. The stabilization process usually entails the use of two solutions which are caustic, and the finished prints are damp and of doubtful permanence. While the materials used in most stabilization process reader-printers tend to be high in contrast and thereby low in exposure latitude, lower contrast stabilization process papers can be obtained and, in some cases, used to good advantage. The one process which might offer the best compromise is the Electrofax process. While it can be assumed that machine costs might be fairly high, one version of the process is completely dry and the prints produced are permanent.

Design and construction

IMAGE SIZE. Image sizes of 7 by 8¼ or 7 by 9⅜ inches are simply too small for the satisfactory reproduction of a large percentage of library microforms. An image size of 11 by 14 inches would immensely increase the utility of a reader-printer for library use. Larger materials could be reproduced at life size and smaller materials could be printed two pages per print. Complete control over print size would be desirable but would add to the cost of the machine. If the machine only delivered two sizes of prints—11 by 14 inches and 8½ by 11 inches—this might be a satisfactory compromise.

MAGNIFICATION CONTROL. As has been brought out repeatedly in the machine analyses, library microtransparencies vary over a wide range of reduction ratios. To cope with the variables in image size thus introduced, a reader-printer must offer virtually complete control over the magnification of any given image.

IMAGE POSITION. The filming of library materials is done in all four of the formats shown in Figure 14. A reader-printer for library use therefore must provide for full rotation of the screen image, and must provide for both vertical and horizontal adjustments of the image position.

FILM-TRANSPORT ASSEMBLY. To eliminate any possibility of scratching, the glass flats which hold the film in plane must be separable and must be *easily* removable for cleaning. Ideally, the flats should automatically separate when the film advance knob is rotated, or an interlock mechanism should be introduced which would make it impossible to advance the film if the flats are closed. Also, the spindles on which the reels are placed should be geared up to at least a 2:1 ratio and the spindle cranks or film advance knob should be large enough in radius to permit easy and rapid rewinding of a 100-foot reel of film.

FOCUSING MECHANISM. The focusing mechanism should operate smoothly and easily and should move the image to either side of an "in-focus" position with a single turn of the hand. It should also be securely mounted so that no lateral shifting of the image occurs during focusing.

PROCESSING. If a process involving the use of solutions (such as the stabilization process) is employed, the solution trays should be easily accessible for filling and easily removable for cleaning with the least possible hazard of spillage. The rollers should also be readily accessible for daily cleaning.

SHEET MICROFILM. Until recently, sheet microfilm has been little used in this country, but the announcement of two important publishing projects in which sheet film will be used has brought this particular microform into a position of considerable prominence.

The design of an efficient reader-printer for microtransparencies, therefore, should provide for the viewing and printing of films in sheet form as well as in roll form.

These recommendations cover the fundamental attributes that a good reader-printer for library use should possess. One could go on to other highly desirable features, but at that point, machine costs would go up sharply. For example, the effect of background density on exposure settings is minimal with the xerographic process. It is also possible with the xerographic process to make a positive print from a positive or from a negative, but xerographic equipment capable of such refinements is very costly. Also, to keep the operation of the machine as simple as possible so that an unskilled person can obtain good results easily, the operation of the machine should be highly automated. Ideally, everything should be on a push-button basis. But such a degree of automation also could be introduced only at a very high cost. Compromises are therefore indicated.

With the exception of the Ross Microreader, no reading and printing device on the market today has been designed to accommodate library microforms. The Filmac 300 comes closest to meeting the basic requirements of a reader-printer for library use, but it appears to have been designed as a universal reader-printer for microtransparencies. Libraries could happily do without some of the features and refinements found in the Filmac 300 and still have a device which would go a great deal further than any other machine in meeting their needs. The lack of good equipment for libraries — and this holds true not only for reader-printers but for many kinds of equipment — is largely a problem of economics. The library market is generally considered by manufacturers to be too small as compared with the market available in the fields of business, industry, and government. While this may be so, manufacturers of reader-printers should remember that the libraries of the land were among the first to make use of microforms and in the course of the past thirty years have built collections of microforms which add up to billions of pages of important research materials. Indeed, manufacturers themselves depend heavily on the resources of research libraries, resources which are often in microform. And every day, in every library sizable enough to have or make use of a photographic service, countless numbers of prints from microforms are being made by what now might quite properly be called the "old-fashioned" methods of silver halide enlarging.

Despite the decided limitations of the reader-printers presently available, many libraries have purchased such machines, because even the partial fulfillment of a pressing need is better than none at all. If more libraries have not purchased reader-printers, one of the primary reasons is that most of the reader-printers available are simply not up to doing the job that needs doing. It might behoove manufacturers of reader-printers to take another look at the library world, its vast holdings of microforms, and its needs.